LIFE WITH DAKTARI

Also by
SUSANNE HART

★

TOO SHORT A DAY:
A Woman Vet in Africa

LIFE
WITH DAKTARI

Two Vets in East Africa

*

SUSANNE HART

THE
COMPANION BOOK CLUB
LONDON

This edition is published by
The Hamlyn Publishing Group Ltd.
and is issued by arrangement with
Geoffrey Bles Ltd. in conjunction
with William Collins, Sons & Co. Ltd.

Made and printed in Great Britain
for the Companion Book Club
by Odhams (Watford) Ltd.
SBN600771199

To Toni
and the elephants

CONTENTS

ACKNOWLEDGMENTS

MY GRATEFUL THANKS are due to my husband, Toni Harthoorn, for his inspiration which made this book possible in the
first place, and for all his drawings; to my daughter Gail, friend
and critic, who once again came to my aid; to many friends,
lovers of wildlife, who have allowed me to use their photographs
and have given me a great deal of help and vital information; to
Pamela Mackenroth, who contributed the drawing on page 5
and worked into the small hours of the night to complete
the typescript.

S. H.

ILLUSTRATIONS

[CONTINUED OVERLEAF]

Pictures nos. 5, 9 and 31 by George Adamson;
8 and 36 by Joy Adamson; 7, 14 and 22 by *East
African Standard*; 6, 10, 11, 12, 13, 15, 16, 17, 19,
23, 24, 25, 26, 28 and 29 by A. M. Harthoorn;
3 and 4 by Charles Hayes; 18 by Bill Holz; 21 by
Johnny Jay, by permission of Paramount; 27 by
Yuilleen Kearney; 32 and endpapers by Howard
Kirk; 2 by Jenny Layard; 34 and 35 by Frank
Minot; 30 by Cynthia Moss; 20 and 33 by
John Seago.

INTRODUCTION

'EVER SINCE I was a small child I wanted to be a vet, in Africa.'

I was thinking aloud, remembering my pre-school days through a haze of bright arc lights, monitor screens and television camera lenses. I recalled my first animal patient, a tiny battered fieldmouse, which had died in spite of my ardent ministrations. My grief had been great, but so had my determination. I had to become a vet so that in future my patients would not die, however fragile they were.

This was the fifth and last programme, the last of the half-hours which I had tried to fill with Africa and its animals and the people who worked among them. I had not intended to say anything about my earliest youth but Joy Whitby, the dynamic B.B.C. Television producer of the children's *Jackanory* series, had insisted.

'So many will want to know how you became a vet and found your way to Africa; it's only natural.'

She was right of course, but how could I crowd it all into five short thirty-minute programmes? I felt honoured to have been asked to bring my experiences back to the very place from which I came: London, my home town, from whose streets I had rescued flea-ridden mongrels and destitute cats which I had taken home to my horrified, bewildered parents who did not share my strange, totally uninherited taste for the animal world; London, among whose higgledy-piggledy streets and grey pavements I had spent two happy, carefree years of college life. Each morning and afternoon I had walked from St. John's

Wood through Regent's Park to the Royal Veterinary College in Camden Town, passing the back of the London Zoo on the way. I loved the Park, yet much as I revelled in the snowy-pink peach blossoms and wealth of daffodils, I grieved daily for the caged inhabitants who appeared to live in misery behind the big fence.

The multi-shaped African animals caught both my imagination and my pity; I longed to see them free and wild and beautiful, as I knew they must be. How I would ever get there and work among them I could not even begin to imagine. There were no links, there was no encouragement and when I had, on one occasion, applied for the job of vet-in-charge of an animal transport ship to Africa, I had been turned down flat for no better reason than that I belonged to the wrong sex!

Yet even then, though quite unbeknown to me, my dream had been set in motion, for the man whom I was to marry eighteen years later had already set his footsteps in the right direction. Toni Harthoorn, who had rejoined the Veterinary College after serving in the war, became a fellow-student during my second year. With the typical abandonment of a seventeen-year-old, I had fallen head over heels in love with the tall, humorous giant, and though our romance did not outlast our college years we remained firm friends and, on parting, kept track of each other's lives by letter. To our intense surprise we both ended up in Africa for entirely different reasons. Toni accepted a University post in Uganda and later moved to Kenya, while I, to the chagrin of my professors who saw yet another female vet going to waste, married a South African and came to Africa that way.

After my two children, Gail and Guy, were born, and having neglected my career for four years, I returned to veterinary practice with many misgivings and great apprehension. Living in a rural area where there was no vet for hundreds of miles helped me considerably; there simply wasn't time for doubt or hesitation when there was so much work to be done. The practice grew very quickly, and with it my confidence in the work which I found I loved as much as ever.

Then my marriage went on the rocks, and the children and I moved to a beautiful mountainous area only fifteen miles away, where once again I put up my veterinary plate. About the time of my status change, Toni, thousands of miles away, was beginning to find a way to immobilize the hitherto elusive, large wild animals, which included elephant, hippopotamus and rhinoceros. As my practice domain bordered on the Kruger National Park, the largest of South Africa's wildlife sanctuaries, I began to orientate myself towards the study of wildlife. I met many authorities on African fauna and flora and made many journeys into different animal sanctuaries. A new kind of world was opening up before me and though I was unaware of it at the time, I was being prepared for yet another phase of my life, one which was to take me much closer to the kind of work I had dreamt of as a student.

'Never in my wildest dreams did I ever imagine that I would be doing something like this.'

Upon the monitor screen in front of me appeared the drawing of a huge elephant, his puzzled and slightly shocked expression evidence that he did not in the least approve of what the tiny recumbent figure under his tail seemed to be doing. I wondered how many of my *Jackanory* viewers, old and young, would doubt the truth of what they were seeing. It seemed ludicrous, right here in London, in a television studio; so unlikely, so very unladylike, and, taken out of context, even hazardous.

Yet it was all true and, moreover, I loved every moment of it. Being at the rear end of such an operation had its reason: I was taking the elephant's temperature, and my posture, under the circumstances, was by far the most practical for the achievement of my purpose.

This transformation—some might call it promotion—from country vet to member of wild animal study team had come upon me most unexpectedly. Eight years after moving into the hills Toni had come to the Kruger National Park to advise on the immobilization of elephant. We had met again and this time had joined forces permanently, after which the children and I had moved north to Kenya. To my surprise—and relief—Toni's ideas on the place of the modern woman, career or no, were somewhat different from mine. His attitude, a mixture of European gallantry and protectiveness (being of Dutch descent) and an earnest desire to give me free rein, provided he held them firmly in his hands, made my new life a complete contrast to my old, for I had lived in reckless independence with no one to see if my feet got wet or my meals were square. Now, suddenly, I rated as a 'dependant,' married to a man who insisted that I was completely unable to take care of myself. He seemed quite certain that my survival up to the time he had, once again, entered my life could only be accredited to the merest chance! Having made a 'decent woman out of me' as he charmingly put it, I now faced new work and different kinds of responsibilities and privileges, including a place in his wild animal ventures. Always on the alert Toni saw to it that I kept my place and took no risks. Only at the very moment when the wild animal we happened to be working on became immobile, was I allowed to come to the front end for the taking of blood from the ear veins, external parasites for the ardent parasitologists, and to assist whoever needed assistance, which was usually everybody at the same time. When the moment came to give the antidote he saw to it that I was out of the way first and safely stowed—like a spare tyre—in the back of the Land-Rover.

'Write it down,' Toni had demanded one day, 'don't waste another minute or you will forget it all.'

I had tried to explain that my days were already overfull, for I was then lecturing, making local television programmes on animal life and practising part-time. I had children to care for, the house to maintain, servants to train and oversee. Apart from anything else, I was married to the most demanding man south of the Sahara who wanted my *every available spare moment!*

'You're practically unemployed,' was his dry comment to my objections. 'Before you married me you maintained a full-time country practice, looked after the children, animals, a farm and a host of visitors. Also, you wrote two books, gave lectures and broadcasts, and still had time to make sumptuous marmalade and home-made bread. Now, with me to look after you and to remind you to do all the things you would otherwise forget, you have plenty of time.'

I gave up after that, for I knew that whatever I said would make no impression. Then I had an idea, one last hope: 'If I write a book about our life and work, then it must be a true account of everything, including you. How do you feel about that?'

'Nonsense,' he stalled, 'no one could possibly be interested in me. Besides, it is indecent to tell the truth.'

'Let me be the judge of that,' I said ominously, suddenly realizing that to write a book might be most revealing to both of us. 'I'll try not to disillusion the world too much, but after all, a few home truths about the real "Daktari" can do no harm. It might bring that bush-vet-scientist image into perspective and give people a truer idea of what his adventure-filled days are *really* like.'

I had tried to tell my television viewers something about 'Daktari' and how it had all begun. The producer was delighted that such a person actually existed, that the television story was based on fact. That the mythical man behind it happened to be my husband made her very happy indeed. Now it all made sense. Television, direct and informal, was one thing, but would I ever be able to recreate the atmosphere, the magic or the grandeur of Africa on paper?

'It will be our book, not mine alone,' I reassured Toni who was beginning to look distinctly nervous at my sudden enthusiasm. 'Nothing will go into print without your approval.'

We had agreed that I would describe some of our adventures, endeavours and excitements, and by so doing portray the magnificence of Africa and the glory of its wild life, if such a thing were ever possible; the challenge and the joy and the heartache that is such an integral part of our life.

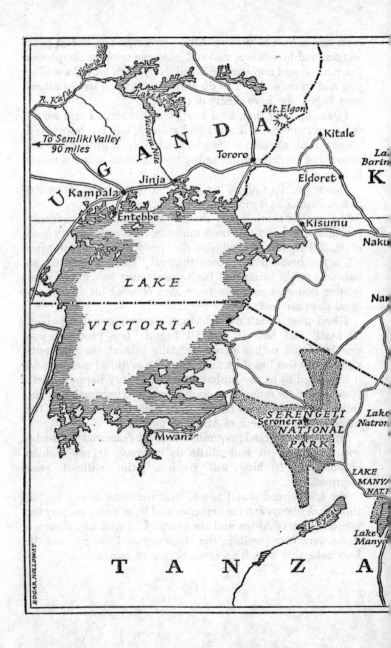

R. Kafu

Victoria Nile

Lake K.

Mt. Elgon

Kitale

To Semliki Valley
90 miles

U G A N D A

Tororo

Eldoret

La
Barin

K

Jinja

Kampala

U

Kisumu

Naku

Entebbe

L A K E

Nar

V I C T O R I A

Na

Mwanza

SERENGETI
NATIONAL
PARK

Seronera

Lake
Natron

LAKE
MANYA
NAT.

L. Eyasi

Lake
Manya

EDGAR HOLLOWAY

T A N Z A

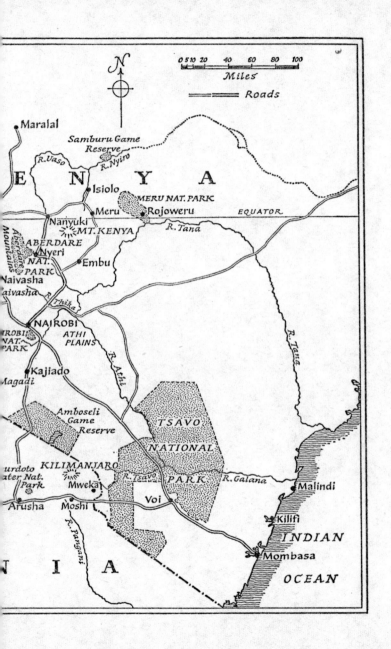

1 *Sex or Coffee*

THE FIRST TIME the telephone rang it was so late and the sound so unfamiliar that I did not recognize it. Toni, blissfully asleep, seemed oblivious of everything about him, his breathing slow and regular while my dream fell into a thousand kaleidoscopic fragments as waves of nightmarish sound engulfed us with relentless discordance.

I sat up and tried to focus on the luminous clock hands on my bedside table: ten minutes to midnight. Surely a newly installed telephone had absolutely no right to ring at such an hour! Besides, who could possibly have discovered our telephone number in a matter of hours?

'It's bound to be a wrong number,' I tried hard to convince myself, 'and perhaps it isn't our phone at all. Maybe it's the neighbours'.'

After a few moments, which seemed like an hour, I decided to take action. Toni would grumble, he would complain and curse the wretched machine, but I would have to risk that. It had been I who had insisted that a telephone be installed in the first place, for life without one, even if I was not practising as a full-time vet, was unthinkable. In my nine years of county vet duty I had developed, among other ills, a disease known as telephone jitters, an occupational affliction which is difficult to throw off. I had developed an eighth sense whereby I seemed to know just when the telephone was about to ring, and knowing it was my lifeline for emergencies I was not able to pluck up the courage to disconnect it.

When we arrived in our University house in Nairobi three months before, the telephone shelf had been empty. I had spent so many hours and days persuading the telephone exchange that they should install one that in the end they did; the phone was put in and actually connected (most unusual) during the same week. Toni had just been getting used to its appearance, was even congratulating me on my success. . . .

I made an effort to clear my brain but it was difficult. We had only gone to bed two hours before and had been completely exhausted. All day we had opened crates, hung paintings, tried to find space for all our belongings. We had cursed all our excess possessions, far more than we really needed. Still, we had been grateful to eat off our beautiful Bosch pottery plates that night and sleep between our own sheets. I touched Toni lightly on the arm, then took his hand.

'Darling,' I said fatuously, 'do you think our telephone is ringing?'

I didn't want to wake him altogether, but just enough to get his opinion on the matter of the persistent sound which was coming through the door. He stirred a little and opened one eye. Our moonlit room, a turmoil of packing cases and wood-wool, bookstacks and wrapping paper, exuded a kind of jumbled cosiness scented with mothballs.

'Turn it off,' Toni murmured, 'go back to sleep.'

What could I do, for the ringing tone seemed to be getting louder and more persistent, seeming to convey a midnight urgency. There was a slim chance that it *might* be important, though I could not really imagine how that could be. We had so newly arrived, like the telephone.

Toni was getting restless. He now sat up, rubbed his eyes, then opened them both. 'Twentieth-century curse,' he muttered, 'who wants a telephone anyway? It used to be so peaceful before they put it in.'

'But now that it is in, you had better answer it,' I urged. 'Maybe it's a call from overseas, from the family.' That made him think for a moment and in the end leap out of bed, almost falling headlong over a crate as he went.

20

'Toni Haithoorn here,' I heard him boom brusquely through the open door. Then I heard his voice change to a more cordial tone and breathed a sigh of relief. Whoever it was, was getting civil treatment; it must at least be a friend or a long standing acquaintance.

'Right,' I heard him say, 'I'll be right over.' He put down the phone and closed the door. 'A case,' he said enigmatically. 'It's Charles Hayes. He says some dogs ganged up on Rufus and have injured him. I'd better go and see.'

'Want me to come?' I asked, as I watched him fling on some clothes.

'No,' he said gallantly. 'You need all the sleep you can get. Just find me the medical case.'

I found the case and opened the front door. How nice to have a man to answer the telephone, and what was more, to go out on night calls. As he started the car I climbed back into bed and revelled in it. He might yet phone and ask me to come and help, but probably, from the sound of it, it would be a wound that could be stitched in the morning, when there was some light to see by. I turned off the light and waited. Outside the window the fruitbat was still sending its radar-like signals, like the rhythmic ping of a strange new world. 'Pinnnnnnnnng.' The first time I heard that weird sound I had woken Toni in alarm. To me it had seemed like some devilish, mechanical device, perhaps buried in our garden, about to blow up like a time-bomb. 'That's only a fruitbat spitting out the pips,' he had said, and had gone back to sleep. Weeks later, Jean Hayes, whom I had met just after my arrival in Kenya, told me why there were no pips to be found on the lawn the next morning. The fruit-bat ate fruit, she had told me, very much amused, but the pips just passed on through, the easy way!

I wondered, as the minutes ticked by, what Toni was doing. Rufus, the young male Situtunga antelope, was kept in a garden enclosure behind the Hayes' home which was only five minutes drive away from our house. He had been brought from Uganda, where these swamp antelope are much more common than in Kenya, as a three-month-old, bright-red, long-haired calf. He had become very tame. They hoped to keep him in Nairobi until he became sexually mature and until they could find him a Situtunga wife. After that they would both go to Crescent Island, the Hayes' recently acquired wild-life sanctuary. We had visited the island, which lies on Lake Naivasha, shortly after arriving in Kenya. Winding upwards and west out of the city environs I had gasped in awe and amazement at the breathtaking sight which met us at the halfway halt at the top: the valley in the earth's crust known as the Rift.

Just after the last bend which opens up the overwhelming vista, stands a tiny church like a rock of the Lord to remind the passer-by that such an unearthly sight as he has just beheld is not a mundane everyday affair but a piece of beauty specially created to put man in touch with his own soul. The volcanic peaks can be seen from this point, their charred black-grey inclines evidence that their eruptions stirred the earth not so very many thousands of years before. Looking down into the thick jungles and the red-tipped aloes reminds one where one is; looking across the Rift Valley, at early morning a haze of softest shades of gold-grey-purple, makes one lose all sense of time and place. Only the white flitting butterflies, arriving in droves as the sun warms the mountainside, bring one back to earth.

Soon the lake, famous throughout the world for its diverse population of birds, appears like a blue void nestling in the valley; then the island, its truly crescent moon form framed by the hills beyond. The reverberating, haunting call of the fish eagle welcomed us as we reached the shore, the white-throat thrown back as he sounded his territorial note. To me, so new to the tropics, he epitomized Africa; he and the yellow-green-stemmed fever-trees, reflecting the burning sun. Flocks of sacred ibis, which I had always thought of as being most rare, were gathering food on the lakeside fields, quite indiffer-ent to our coming. The saddlebill stork, largest and most spec-tacular of all storks, had chosen the island as his home. The

'Tommy' gazelle were multiplying, reedbuck, duiker and waterbuck had found their way into the marshland stretches when the water-level was low enough to expose the causeway. Crescent would be just the place for Rufus and if he had a mate to anchor him he might not be tempted to swim away . . . that is, if he survived the damage of a pack of dogs. How often during the course of my practice years, had I been asked to repair the wounds inflicted by those sharp, long canine teeth. . . .

If the Hayes' kept an antelope in their garden perhaps other city-dwellers kept similar creatures in theirs. It might yet transpire that our wildlife practice, apart from our outgoing up-country calls, might be more substantial than we had imagined.

Why was Toni taking so long? I did not want to fall asleep in case he called me and in any case I wanted to be awake enough to be able to talk coherently to him when he returned. He had left a whole hour ago and by this time was probably drinking coffee with Charles, with both of them taking it in turn to put the wildlife world to rights. I put on the light; it was almost two o'clock. I got up and put on the kettle, ashamed of my thoughts, determined to have the teapot ready for the time Toni came home, tired and thirsty, perhaps, from his midnight case.

How my life had changed, I thought, as I watched the kettle boil. For six months, since Toni and I had been married in London, I had lived the most fantastic life, beginning in America. Toni was long overdue for his study leave and had been awarded a Rockefeller Fellowship. Though only one man's allowance, we lived on it in comfort for six months— and later on so did Gail and Guy, two growing and permanently ravenous children. We were being loaned two cars and a house, and lived like kings—I, lazy and carefree, enjoying all that Colorado had to offer between spring and autumn of that year.

It had been like a six-month honeymoon! The children had, for the first three months, remained with their father in South Africa and continued their schooling. That had given us time to adjust a little to our new surroundings—and to each other. Toni, acting as courier for M99, the morphine-like substance which up to that time had only been in use in Africa, for the immobilization of large wild animals, had not told anyone that he was bringing a four-day-old wife. It had been a little awkward since he had not, until the last moment, known for certain whether I would be able to come at all, married or otherwise. But the news preceded us across the Atlantic. At a conference held in Cambridge on the day after our marriage, a very good friend, who had in fact asked Toni to transport the drug in the first place, had whispered the burning question in my ear. 'You two look so radiant, it's unnatural; tell me, how long HAVE you been married?'

I'm not sure what Toni's answer would have been had he been the one who was asked. He was feeling extraordinarily shy about the fact that the girl with him was a brand-new spouse, and did his best to pass us off as an 'old married couple.' 'Thirty hours, but please don't mention it to anyone or my life won't be worth living.'

'Of course not,' he had nodded, enormously pleased with his secret, but nevertheless he had made it his business to see that our hosts in New York knew about us, and that, on arrival, after being shepherded to one of the most sumptuous hotels, we would be left in peace for the weekend.

That had been the beginning of an amazing journey. Wherever we went we met kindness and generosity. We toured the country, covering a great part of it, for Toni lectured in fifteen veterinary schools. We saw bears in the snow, blinking in the sunlight as they emerged from their hibernations; we saw streamlined cities, and deserted beautiful rockland heights and lake-lands which America's millions had not yet discovered or did not want to know. Eventually, when the children arrived, we settled in at Fort Collins so that Toni could continue his researches into the effect of an antidote to M99 with an equally odd code number, M285! He had chosen Colorado State University because, as he said jokingly, it seemed to be more like Africa than anywhere else—5,000 feet, the Nairobi altitude, and in the distance, snow-covered mountains whose refreshing breeze cooled the mid-summer air of the West.

What a change it had been *not* to practise, not to be a public servant but a lady of leisure, drinking in new experiences and new horizons. I knew this could not continue and secretly hoped that there would be some interesting work to do in my new homeland. But what and where I had no idea. It would not be full-time vet practice, that I knew already. Toni had insisted that I had *him* to take care of now and that I would be finding it a full-time job! But there might be other things, exciting new fields of wildlife conservation, more writing—that is, if I found anything to write about!

If! And here I was, in Nairobi, barely unpacked, involved in wild animal practice and flights into the unknown in small planes piloted by men who rarely knew the way better than I did. My days may have seemed very full before, yet in the light of what I had already discovered since I had married Toni, any life, however busy, is only part-time if there is not a man to take care of.

At last I heard the door. Toni came breezing in, swinging his black medical bag as if it were an umbrella. He was humming a tune, a sure sign that he was either very upset or very happy, and from the expression on his face I judged the latter. 'Like some tea?' I suggested. 'It's already made.'

'Let's have it in bed, and I'll tell you about Rufus,' he said as he closed the front door. He had found a deep tear-wound on the back of the thigh and an injury on the chin and horn caused by his efforts to escape when the dog-pack had burst in upon him. 'Time tomorrow to stitch it and clean it up,' he added. 'It will take some of your best invisible mending to restore the tissues. I have given him an antibiotic injection and packed the wound with acriflavine-soaked gauze.'

Late though the hour was, we were now wide awake, and so was Skimpy, disturbed by the commotion, crying for milk. I suppose it was only fair; if we were going to have a late (early) tea session, then she should also be allowed to satisfy her thirst. Once more I got up and this time Toni stayed in bed. 'Worse than having a baby,' he complained. 'If she were a real baby at least I'd have somewhere to dry my socks!'

Poor Toni, the bat-eared fox did sleep in the airing cupboard at night, the only consistently warm place in the whole house. I took her out and gave her part of an already prepared bottle; not her full six o'clock ration, but just enough (I hoped fervently) to keep her quiet until getting-up time, only four hours away.

Bobby Cade, curator of the animal orphanage of the Nairobi National Park, had asked me to take her. There had been a litter of six born in the fox's lair, two of which turned out to be weaklings. I had never seen them at close quarters before. Though the father fox, unlike other canine animals, fiercely guarded his brood, Bobby allowed me to enter the enclosure, instructing me to move slowly and quietly. I fell in love with the two runts at once. They lay huddled together, alone and neglected, the mother quite disinterested in any but the four well-matched lusty pups. I picked them up and stroked them; they had the smallest pointed faces and softest fur, enormous ears, ochre-grey-brown bodies with a bushy black-tipped tail. 'Take them,' Bobby had said. 'If you don't, they will die anyway. Not much chance of survival,' he added as an afterthought, 'but try if you like.'

I wanted to try very much, though one of the two seemed hardly alive. I got a baby bottle of the doll variety and a teat

26

and Bobby helped me to compose a formula. We decided on a human vitamin supplement and a feeding routine. It would be a four-hourly schedule and lots of warmth and love and care. My family were delighted when they saw them but sad when the tiniest died during the first night. The second, though minute, seemed more robust, and we named her 'Skimpy.' She grew well and fast, body and voice. Her call, sometimes issuing from the strangest, most remote places, was a God-send, since without it we might often have spent hours searching for her. How like a bird it sounded. Its intensity was so great that the hovering eagle, its natural enemy, must have found it very easy prey; that is, if sound as well as sight helped them to locate their food.

'Come to bed,' Toni commanded from the bedroom, 'or it won't be worth it.' Four hours would help stave off exhaustion a little, yet when I did eventually climb into bed I found it hard to get to sleep. Toni turned off the light, bid me a tender good night and dropped off. I listened for the sonar bat, now a familiar sound, but heard soft rain falling instead. On the roof, in the trees, on the ground.

We had arrived in our new home country in the rain. Kenya, so beautiful, looked drab and limp and unwelcoming to me on that October day. Toni had travelled ahead of us from Rome where my sister, more devoted to the world of Arts than Wildlife, was living at the time and where we had all been subjected to a few days of 'seeing ruins.' We saw so many, interspersed with glorious cathedrals and ancient cobblestone squares, that by the time we touched down in Nairobi we were exhausted. Looking back upon it I see that it was just if not intended revenge, for I had so often 'dragged' my sister into wildlife sanctuaries which she abhorred and which she has sworn never to enter again.

I spent my first month in devoted domesticity—just that. In the past I had always interspersed my work with domestic labours, such as ministering to the children and farm animals, arranging our menus, caring for and organising our faithful servants and entertaining our friends. I now devoted myself

27

ENTIRELY to such things, and felt the strangeness and impermanence of it at once. I walked everywhere on foot, for our house, though attached to a large, treed and incredibly wild garden, stood only ten minutes from the city centre.

Walking is the way to discover a city, discover its pulse and its rhythm. I found Nairobi utterly exciting and exotic. A combination of East and West, a blending of colour and personality into one modern throbbing heart of Africa, fringed by a country which contained a people struggling for existence and advancement. From the Eastern incense-rich streets of the Bazaar, I would wander across to the international society or tall modern buildings; embassies, information centres and charming, well-appointed coffee houses where one could sit and listen and look with pleasure and with wonder at the variety of homo sapiens. All this to the accompaniment of the most delicious aroma of Kenya coffee, said to be the best in the world.

I grew to love Nairobi and Kenya more quickly than I would ever have imagined, especially after the first impression on our day of arrival, when the heavens had poured forth their abundance. That day, I had been nervous, to say the least, yet the children had hardly been able to contain their excitement. My greatest misgivings had sprung from the uncertainty of HOW the new marriage would work, knowing full well that much of success or failure would depend on me. Apart from anything else, I had forgotten how to live with a man in every sense, and having been dragged by Fate out of my furrow of glorious complacence, I had at first resented having to give consideration to another demanding and ever-present human being. He, living in his world of science at cloud-level from which he rarely descended, was more than a little shocked that I expected him to descend to me at frequent intervals, including all mealtimes!

During the first month we were so busy that we hardly noticed we were married, except at meal-times and at night in bed. I still found it strange to climb into bed with a six-foot-six individual who pulled the sheets and blankets in his direction whenever he moved. Neither of us snored, which made the nocturnal adjustments, often the most difficult, easier. The children had to unlearn the habit of charging into the bedroom as they had been wont to do in my bachelor days, and seemed to find it no hardship. Guy stopped, by special request, walking entirely on his heels in the dawn hours of the morning. Gail began to accept the fact that she had to share me with a grown-up man when hitherto she had shared me only with her small brother.

After a month of voluntary domesticity, I decided that the time had come to go to work. Toni, appreciative of what I was doing to the house, realizing that I was nearing the end of my domestic researches and that I needed a fuller life, encouraged me to break out of the home routine but didn't know in which direction. 'Hope you don't get into mischief,' he mocked, 'or join the coffee and bridge élite of Nairobi. What do you want to do?' I didn't know the answer to his question then, but I was sure I would not be playing bridge to keep myself busy. Besides, my father had, years before discouraged me from playing a card game, which he felt was well beyond my I.Q. 'You just haven't that kind of logic,' he had said, to my dismay. My mother, also a bridge expert, had kindly, but firmly, agreed with his dictum. It was then, as a third-year vet student, that I had turned to poker and had become very adept at it, thus vindicating my genius at cards and blaming my parents whenever I could for having driven me to gambling!

'I am going out to look for work,' I had announced one morning. 'Today is the day, so don't be surprised at anything.' Perhaps it was the magic of the Jacaranda blue or the sight of the first European stork, saluting as he hovered over the river pool at the bottom of our garden. It was English autumn but here it was spring, time for action and new horizons.

'But what will you do, where will you go?' Toni looked a little worried at my champagne mood and was quite dumbfounded when I confessed that I didn't know the answer but would think about it the moment he left.

I watched his figure disappearing down the rocky incline among the Frangipani blossoms. The preclinical school was only seven minutes walk away—seven minutes, that is, of his long-leg time, but nearly twice as long for me!

When he had become a tiny figure among the trees, I poured myself some more tea, took it down into the morning sun, and thought. As I wasn't going to practise full-time, it had to be something else. It would be nice if I could continue my children's broadcasts, or write more stories about animals.

The only way to find that kind of work was to go to the Voice of Kenya, the local broadcasting station, whose receiving towers were almost visible from our house, and make personal contact. I gathered together a few samples of my stories, put on walking shoes and set off, excited as any explorer on a new mission. Within minutes of leaving our house I reached the 'University Way,' mingling with the gay crowd on the wide pavements, a cross section of humanity of every colour and creed. Exquisite Indian lady students in saris and Punjabi dress, turbaned Sikhs and unturbaned sallow-skinned faces of the East mixed freely with Africans from every part of the vast continent. Some primitive, some sophisticated with books under their arms, headed for class, beggars, pathetic, entreating, businessmen, tradesmen, shoppers, uncaring of the cripples on the pavements. Large Mercedes cars, tiny rattle-traps, convertibles—everything going at horrific speed and with relentless disregard for their fellows on the road or on the pavement. I had heard Nairobi is a most dangerous city to drive in. Very soon, as soon as I had my own car, I would be part of the road-hogs and the screaming-brake mob!

Coming so recently from South Africa, I yet found no strangeness in the multi-racial atmosphere and way of life of Kenya. I had always had friends among the African and Asian community and the code of life had affected me very little. 'Why don't you vote?' my community-conscious sister often asked me. 'How can you live in a country and be such an irresponsible citizen? You don't even read the newspapers!'

'But how can I possibly decide who to vote for, when I know

so many charming, good people of each party. Rather than make the wrong decision, isn't it better just to abstain?' I had no political aspirations or understanding, had never had time for conscience campaigns or party fireworks, I had left those to other, more nation-building individuals whom I admired immensely for their ability of knowing which way to cast their vote.

Voice of Kenya was guarded and protected and I had to state my business to a very charming, uniformed man on duty, who gave me a slip to be signed and returned, then took me up the winding stairs to my destination——Children's Broadcasts. Ann Greer, in charge of that section, was delighted by my promise to bring her children's stories adapted for radio. Ever pregnant, delightful, fresh complexioned, forthright, she was a well-spoken Alice-in-Wonderlandish sort of person, just what I had always expected to find in a Children's Hour centre of operations. She was very interested to hear of my previous work with schoolchildren, live broadcasts including animals, where question time was the great and essential feature, the new and vital approach for attracting the young into the world of animals.

Writing for children had come out of itself, for my twosome had been reared on my own invented stories from the time they could understand what I was telling. I had had no intention of ever committing them to paper until one day my son Guy, then very small, and at the argumentative and critical stage, had interrupted my story about the zebra who had lost her stripes by insisting that I had told it differently on the previous occasion. 'No, no, that's not how it happened,' he said over and over again.

'But I made it up in the first place,' I pleaded, 'so I can do what I like with it.'

'Oh no you can't!' Gail, older by eighteen months did not agree at all. 'Once it is told one way it has to stay that way. *I'll* finish it for you.' And so, in spite of the fact that she had the mumps and was supposed to feel very poorly indeed, she had commenced the story of Zoe the Zebra all over again, and

I had to admit in the end that she was right and that I had been wrong.

'Why don't you write it all down?' my little nephew, Alan, had said, 'like you wrote down the story of the runaway sandals for my birthday. Then no one can quarrel about it.'

I did write them down and finally after they had been published, I had adapted them for radio. I wrote more and more and tested my material on many children of different ages. They and they alone were my judges. If they wept too profusely, or if they did not once change expression, into the waste-paper basket the pages would go, torn to shreds. It would take me a long time to become a confident children's writer, so confident that I myself would know what was suitable without consulting my infantile judges.

I was deeply immersed in my new venture when Toni came home for lunch that day. The idea that there was work to do, that someone actually *wanted* something that I was about to create, electrified me into immediate action. Instead of waiting for my new spouse on the doorstep with open arms, lunch neatly laid out, he found my head immersed in the typewriter among reams of foolscap paper.

'How about lunch and me?' he had said, a little hurt. He encouraged me to work, but he also expected me to be 'just there' when he needed me. That was often, daily and constantly, not only giving help with his own experiments and wildlife research but also at home and in bed. When it was coffee time, coffee had to be there, plenty of it and piping hot. When it was time for sex, something similar applied and he certainly hated to be kept waiting!

There was promise of turbulent days ahead, but nothing that could not be overcome with humour and patience. The ability to laugh at and with each other is what would count in the end and if we managed that, then there was nothing to fear—even if I did sometimes forget to bake a cake or omit to serve coffee at the correct moment.

'Hey, wake up!'

'There he goes again,' I thought sleepily. 'I wonder what he

The author

Barrie was particularly keen on elephant work

At the edge of the Rojowero River

wants now?' My sex and coffee dreams merged into stark reality. Jenny, our maid from Uganda, must have been knocking on the door for some time.

'Karibu' (Come in), Toni had called lustily, and each time I wondered anew how his vocal organ could stand the strain of such violent early morning usage.

'Don't move.' A full cup of steaming liquid was balanced more or less above my head, and above it Toni's grinning, unshaven face. 'Can you manage?' he said invitingly. 'It's just the right temperature. Then we can discuss what we are going to do to Rufus, and when.'

Between sips we planned the day, giving our veterinary job two hours. I was helping Toni with his research work at the laboratory at the time and still had to finish that week's radio play. I HAD to bake a cake to keep the children happy—and some of our own special high-protein bread, which many of our friends, who shared our lunch hour, were beginning to enjoy with us. Toni had warned me that our house would never turn into the sort of free-for-all menage I had kept before where people and animals, friend, stray or sick, had always been welcome. My courage had flagged a little at his pronouncement, yet deep down I knew that if I could make him really happy, even try to rise to his cloud level sometimes, then anything could happen—and it did!

2 *Flying Vets*

LUNCHTIME HAD, within the short settling-in period of one month, become 'open house' for our friends, most of them involved in some sort of wildlife work. They either lived in or around Nairobi, came from Reserves or Parks, farms in out-lying districts, even from as far afield as Tanzania or Uganda. Many were visitors from other countries, who either knew Toni or had heard of or corresponded with him and wanted to exchange or gain new knowledge. Gradually our circle of friends and acquaintances widened and included many fasci-nating, learned and often eccentric personalities whose company we enjoyed enormously and from whom I learnt a great deal about wildlife investigation and management and controversy. It was a privilege to sit in on the many discussions that took place between 12.30 and 2 p.m., when anyone who cared to was welcome to come and join our informal lunch.

I discovered that Nairobi is not only a busy, thriving city but also in many respects one of the crossroads of the world. From film magnates to hunters with gun or camera, conservationists, scientists or just lovers of the wild—they all came to be part of the wealth, the unknown, almost unstudied wealth of Eastern Africa:–its wild animals.

Thus it came about one day that I found a tall rosey-cheeked, bespectacled young man in bush clothes in our still very unfurnished lounge. As I had not the remotest idea who he was, I decided to break the tension at once and introduce myself. 'I'm Sue, Toni's new wife,' I said, holding out my hand. 'So glad to see you. Toni won't be long; can I get you a beer?'

He sprang to his feet and told me he was Ted Goss, and that he would love a beer. He had come to see us both; he had heard that I was also a vet, but would postpone telling the purpose of his errand till Toni arrived. He was very easy to chat to and did not in the least mind a haphazard conversation between kitchen and lounge while I put some lunch together. He told me a little about Meru Game Reserve, and said he was a bachelor. I rather gathered that he intended to remedy this soon, and that he was going on a long journey to do it. He seemed a very determined young man, in more ways than one, and I secretly wondered what sort of wife he had chosen to share his lonely life north-east of Mount Kenya. Would she be large and freckled, with strong legs that could carry her for miles through the thick undergrowth, or a rural girl that knew how to make goat cheese? He might on the other hand have chosen a sophisticated, immaculately dressed white huntress with a wide-brimmed hat to protect her fair skin. I knew so little about Ted, it was hard to judge his taste; as I discovered later, to my delight, his choice was far superior to anything I had imagined, and quite out of the ordinary.

Toni arrived at last and broke up my dreams of the Goss romance. He was very glad to see Ted and ravenous, as always. Both men followed me as I wheeled the trolley full of lunch on to the veranda, facing our beautiful woodland vista. 'That's all you'll get,' I said to Ted. 'Our daily midday fare consists of home-made bread and some things to go on it and round it.' Ted, his appetite as large as Toni's, was about to say something polite as he began to tuck in but Toni interrupted his thought: 'She uses calf-rearing nuts, layers, mash, sawdust and anything else she can find to put in it. It's a good square meal.'

Poor Ted, knowing by now that we were vegetarians, didn't know what to believe. He smiled a weakly sort of smile, not knowing if his eccentric host was serious.

'Now, Ted,' I came to the rescue, 'does *he* really look as if he is living on calf nuts and sawdust? One day,' I added with a warning note to Toni, who was amusing himself hugely, 'one day someone really will believe you and get acute psychological indigestion as a result. And who do you think will get the blame for it?'

Time was running out. Between mouthfuls Ted explained why he had come, and he had to do some fast talking to get it all into the next twenty minutes. (He was about to get final permission to import six 'white' square-lipped rhinoceros from Zululand into Kenya, a tremendous victory after years of negotiations with the authorities.)

First, he wanted help and advice for the last stage of his 'white rhinoceros' mission. Secondly, he had a message for us from George Adamson, whose eldest male lion was in dire need of veterinary attention. That, indeed, was my first real contact with a world about which I had already read, the world of the Adamsons and their leonine tribe; it was also the first call into the wild since our return from the United States.

Toni knew both George and Joy Adamson for he had met them in the days when George was still a game warden in the northern frontier station at Isiolo. Toni had been staying with John Seago, the world's gentleman trapper, while on a zebra immobilization exercise, and Joy had invited them to their home. This had been in 1958, when darting techniques were in their infancy and when the idea of safe wild animal capture was remote and undreamt of. The field of wildlife study, when prior killing would no longer be necessary, was a challenge which captured Toni's attention and tested his scientific knowledge and perseverance for years to come.

Step by step he introduced new substances for each new project as it arose: the study of the kob antelope in Uganda's Semliki Valley where our friend Hal Buechner was working; then Kariba Dam, man-made calamity as far as the animals were concerned, the first rescue operation of any magnitude which had necessitated the use of immobilising drugs. Without them the moody, territorial black rhinoceros might never have been captured and moved to the mainland.

Then came 'Operation White Rhino' in Zululand, as a result of which Ted Goss was about to import a small herd into Kenya.

The kob in Lugari, in north-western Kenya, were rescued in small numbers from the encroachment of the peasant farmers who moved into the settlement schemes. Giraffe, interfering with cultivation, leopard who had become stock killers, rhino threatened by poachers, were now moved to protected areas. The study of wildlife from weight measurement to physiological investigations, to marking for behavioural and range-management studies, had become part of land use and wildlife research. For the veterinarian and the game warden the capture of wild animals served many purposes.

Instead of having to condemn an animal to death for stock-killing, it was possible to immobilise it and examine it. When lions suffer from injury, such as a thorn in the paw, they will obviously kill whatever is easiest to save themselves the labour of hunting the wary prey. The treatment of wild animals after immobilization had been the latest development. The different responses of animals to drugs according to species, age and sex were only beginning to be investigated. Others had learnt the techniques, but that did not lessen the work: letters poured in from all over the world: from polar bears in the Arctic, to elephants in Ceylon. The whole world seemed entranced with this new concept of wildlife work.

One of the many who had become absorbed in this aspect of conservation and who already had a deep interest in Africa was Ivan Tors, the American film director, who had created the famous 'Flipper' series, the story of a dolphin. He had, while travelling in Zululand, heard of Toni's work with the 'white', square-lipped rhinoceros and had also met Ian Player, Chief Conservator, who headed the greatest immobilising team in Africa at that time. Rolling the Player-Harthoorn image into one, he created the now famous *Daktari* programmes for television, his daktari being a handsome, rugged, infallible bush-vet/ranger scientist, as unreal and as unscientific as he is fascinating.

37

Daktari, after all, *does* only mean 'doctor' and is a Swahili word. The aura of the 'daktari' and his stethoscope followed us wherever we went. We did not attempt to leave our centre of operations without our equipment, for to have done so would have been thoughtless and irresponsible. Either a dog had been savaged by a baboon, or the game warden had a sick orphan animal. A herd-boy had been bitten by a snake, a motorist had just been stung by a bee and had discovered he was allergic. One could never be anonymous, for to be part of the medical profession, human or otherwise, places a very definite duty upon one's shoulders. One can never pretend not to know how to help, for that kind of attitude would be a direct contravention of the vow we took on qualifying as veterinarians.

Most vets are Daktaris, and in the wilderness, in the vast expanses where there are no hospitals, dressing stations or doctors, the help of a medico, veterinary or otherwise, is sought by anyone who might need medical attention. You have only to put up your tent. The bush telegraph, fastest communication system on earth, will pass the message from man to man, family to family. 'Daktari is here!' For this reason we always brought other than only animal medicines, though many medicaments suit both. Wound ointments, bandages, antiseptic, snake-bite anti-serum, anti-malarial drugs. Those in need did not in the least mind being treated by a vet—though this applies even in the midst of civilization. In the latter, however, the vet is usually the last resort, while in the bush the first daktari to arrive is the one to do the job.

'I'll fly you both up in my plane,' Ted offered. 'I'll fetch you next weekend if you can come.'

Toni sat thinking, brooding, and his answer was surprisingly evasive. 'I'll let you know before you leave tomorrow,' he said; I knew what he was thinking and somehow I had to make Ted understand too. Since we had seen his friend, Barrie Chappell, crash before our very eyes, we had not flown in a small plane, not under bush conditions anyway. It would take time for him to make a decision, and I know that he wanted to discuss it with me alone. Toni got up, excused himself to go and look at some lecture notes, which gave me a chance to explain to Ted why Toni didn't want to fly in small planes.

Ted had heard about the accident the previous March, the day after I had arrived on a lightning visit to make up my mind whether or not I should marry my old college-mate. I told Ted what had happened; he had not realized how deeply we were both involved. The details were still so vivid, and probably always would be for everyone who was there on that tragic Sunday.

Barrie Chappell had not only been a keen, energetic game warden with go-ahead ideas, he was a great hope for wildlife research and conservation. He was so keen to learn the right way to do things, and Toni spent many weekends with him showing him the darting technique, and the proper use of drugs in immobilization work. Barrie wanted to follow scientific methods, at least as easy as the rough-shod methods adopted by others who insisted on forging ahead in their own way, without skilled help or advice.

I was new to Kenya, that was true. But I had, in the short time I had spent there, gained a good picture of that world in which he moved, for which he worked so ardently. Barrie was also Toni's friend. The day he crashed, a Sunday, he was very tired, had had too little sleep, too many guests, too many responsibilities. He had only just got his wings and needed every fraction of alertness for his spotting flights. We were driving towards the place where he had spotted a rhino cow and calf, and saw him hovering so low that it made me shudder.

That was it, the end of a young life. Perhaps Toni felt responsible, felt that he should have stopped him from going. He did try; I was there with him before he set off for the airstrip. But he didn't want to let us down: John Seago, Tony Parkinson,* Toni and me.

In a way, it was on the day of Barrie's death that my own fate was decided. Tragedy and disaster, the urgent need to pull together in an emergency, brought Toni and me very

* A note about John Seago and Tony Parkinson will be found in Chapter 10.

39

close. John Seago, who wept tears of shock and grief as Barrie lay dying, Tony Parkinson who went with me to tell Barrie's wife, were all part of a team who had desperately tried to save a man's life. 'In sorrow as in joy'—the priest would say; well, here already was some of the sorrow.

Ted sat listening intently. He was a superb pilot, as we were soon to discover, and he must have felt very deeply about Barrie's death. Any pilot-game warden would, and Ted was a game warden. He had developed a unique Reserve under his sole care, for Meru Game Reserve was the first sanctuary ever established by an African District County Council. This is where George Adamson lived with his lions, and where his wife Joy, fifteen miles from his camp, was making a study of cheetah.

'I understand,' said Ted quietly. 'He feels that flying in small planes is dangerous, and he doesn't want you to be involved To me,' he smiled to himself, and when he did his face was that of an enthusiastic schoolboy, 'to me it is far safer up there than on the ground. Especially in Nairobi traffic. Don't know which is more dangerous, being a driver or a pedestrian. In the city, I always feel as though I am caged. Just give me the sky and the bush country. I'd rather face an elephant than a Sikh driver.'

Little did he know how soon his own life would be hanging on a fine thread—because of an elephant. But he didn't think of danger, for he, as Barrie had, faced it daily and gladly. It was his chosen life, and nothing else would do. 'Barrie would have wanted to die in the line of duty,' he said with feeling. 'What better way is there to go?'

'I agree, and I assure you, we'll be taking off with you on Friday noon. Let me speak to Toni alone first. It's like getting back on a horse when you've had a bad fall. It's the only way to make a comeback.'

Only five minutes to go and Ted had to do some fast talking. Toni had returned, lecture notes under his arm, and he leaned back, cup in hand, to listen. Ted's dream was coming true. He wanted six white rhinoceros, three pairs, in his beloved

Meru, and there was only one way to do it: to import them from Zululand, a southern game sanctuary area in South Africa, and to introduce them, step by step, into their new environment. The greatest difficulty was not the change of climate, altitude or latitude. Nor was it a shipping problem, or one of finance. The greatest stumbling block had been to overcome the political barriers between South and East Africa, for in recent years they had broken all links. Since Uhuru, since Kenya had become independent and free, she would no longer trade with South Africa, for the latter still subjugated her coloured citizens, and there seemed little hope of a change in policy.

Ted, undaunted, had for years fought for the re-establishment of the white rhino species in Meru. Situated north-east of Mount Kenya, under 200 miles from Nairobi, it was nevertheless inaccessible, for the road was extremely bad, the last section so rough that it was suicide for any vehicle except the most robust. There was one self-help camp, one now almost derelict lodge and very little publicity that attracted visitors. Yet wildlife was plentiful and the setting breath-takingly beautiful. Ted knew that he needed another attraction, something rare that no other game sanctuary possessed. He knew of the white rhino operation, of Toni's work through which the white southern rhinoceros had been dispersed to many parts of Africa and the world. One species must never be compressed into a single locality.

Not long before some had been introduced into the Rhodesian Kyle Dam and thrived. They had reached the Kruger National Park, and were breeding. A different 'white' species existed in the Sudan, the West Nile area of Uganda and Garamba region of the Congo, only 1,500 miles away from Meru Reserve. Why should they not also exist in a part of Africa which was very like Zululand? Why should he not fight to accept the free gift of six rhino which he had been offered?

Ted told us of his struggles and hopes as briefly as possible so as to put us in the picture. Later, when there was more time and we were on his own home ground, he told us the details of operation rhino. Once the rhinos arrived there might be other difficulties, such as disease, attacks by the tse-tse fly. What should he do to immunize them? Should he wait till they arrived or not? We sorted out the problems as best we could in such a short time. We also promised to take advice from those who had some previous experience with rhinos in South Africa. Scientists who had established a disease picture in previous years, especially in the early days when Zululand was being established as a game preservation area.

Meanwhile there was much to do, that was, provided I could successfully sort out the initial problem of flying. I had to arrange for friends to come and stay to look after the children, get together our veterinary tackle, stock up with food for the family, make sure the servants were organized, pay the electricity before it was cut off (which had happened in double quick time once before) and deliver one script to Voice of Kenya.

That meant each moment counted, and no time to lose. We promised to meet at Wilson Airport the next day no later than noon, and if we decided not to go we would let Ted know in good time. Toni drove off in one direction and Ted in another in his Toyota, which his scout had driven in for repairs and supplies. I returned to the study and began to type—to meet my radio commitment—the story of 'Gruff the Lion', who had lost his mane. As I typed, my mind was already on our patient in Meru, George Adamson's lion who had a bad eye, and who was probably feeling very sorry for himself—and perhaps a little grumpy too.

Gail and Guy were terribly excited when we told them where we were going. They made the best of having to stay behind and, in fact, seemed quite glad, since our American Peace Corps friends, Don and Kae Dakin, were coming to stay again, and there was no one they would rather have to take care of them—or to take care of! 'Please, please bring back his autograph,' begged Guy, 'and Joy Adamson's too, if you see her. Won't you take my "Elsa" books for her to sign?'

I was just as thrilled at the idea of meeting them, though I tried not to show it too much. After all, it was meant to be a working trip and one isn't supposed to be skipping excitedly around when one attends a lion in the middle of the bush. If one did, then the client might well decide to get another vet, one that was just a little calmer. A lion with a sore eye would need a quiet, steady Daktari, one that exuded confidence and strength—or appeared to!

Ted had asked us to take instruments, just in case we found the eye so bad that we would feel justified in removing it; a drastic step! That meant careful planning, and, as I had always done previously in large animal practice, it meant step by step visualizing of surgical procedure. How recent were my memories of Lowveld practice, given up for a steady, less hectic, predictable life in Kenya. And here I was, taking up my veterinary reins again, already occupied to the full with promise of a television series in the New Year, freelance vet work at the orphanage of the Nairobi National Park, a New Year teaching post to help out at the U.N. Institute, and probably many other unseens. Life in the Lowveld seemed mild and lazy compared to this. What would it be like in one year from now, when I had really 'dug in'?

My dear mother, who had been most perturbed about my work with domestic bulls, who had been adverse to the immobilizing ventures with my husband-to-be, what would she say if, looking down from heaven, she saw what we were planning to do? At least she had trusted Toni implicitly, though why, I never did understsnd! It must have been that dignified, lean look he wore, and the way he had bent down to kiss her with smiling eyes that held real affection for his future mother-in-law.

'Why didn't you marry him twenty years ago?' she used to tease after Toni and I had met again. He had impressed her so much even then. Especially the way he used to do his hair, looking into the top of the dining-room dresser mirror, the one which no one else ever reached or dusted. She seemed to have been consoled greatly by the thought that I would be taken care of by someone who was big and strong and chivalrous. I suppose a lion, an elephant or a rhinoceros was neither here nor there; it was the independence and recklessness, the aloneness that she wanted me to lose.

I laid the instruments out carefully, ticked them off as I rechecked, and put them in a drum to be sterilized. I put the drugs, ointments and dressings into a case. I checked the contents of the medical bag—not my old derelict, but Toni's black one, the one we now used together when we practised. I found my old, white jacket and plastic apron, and felt a little nostalgic at the sight of them. I had been given nine happy, full years, and in a way I missed the constant challenge of mixed country practice. Wildlife practice would be exciting, but sporadic, mainly because Toni did not want me to put up a plate again. Already there had been people with dogs and cats, inquiries for horses, sick cows that had somehow found me. And I had been forced to refuse. It was full-time work or a husband.

I preferred the husband!

3 *Zoo in Reverse*

'THERE WON'T BE ROOM to swing a cat,' Ted said as we climbed into the waiting Cessna. And he was right. By the time we had packed in spares for his vehicles, staple foods to keep body and soul together, our personal bag, two medical bags, vegetables and fruit, and two boxes of food for the Adamsons, there wasn't room to swing a mouse. I felt familiar butterfly twinges of apprehension deep down in my stomach (Toni has always denied their anatomical origin), yet longed for the blessed coolness of the upper strata as the midday heat haze danced and shimmered on the tarmac. I didn't have to wait for very long. After checking and rechecking his instrument panel, rather in the manner in which I had checked and rechecked my instrument bag, we taxied to the end of the runway, turned, gave the engines a last minute spurt, closed the windows, checked seat-belts and moved forward, leaving the ground almost imperceptibly.

What a relief! As I saw the glint of tall, white buildings behind us, I imagined the city turmoil and the lunch-hour rush and gave thanks for the traffic-free lanes of the sky. We headed north towards 17,000-foot snow-topped Mount Kenya, passing over thinning habitations, deep green coffee orchards, spiky pineapple fields and thatched huts of tidy new settlement schemes.

Within thirty minutes even that rustic world was left behind, and the mountain rose up to our left, a cloud-curl touching the peak. We had risen 3,000 feet and it was getting deliciously cool. Altitude—8,000 feet above sea level.

Toni sat in front and I was left alone with my thoughts and the luggage. I could see his jaws moving up and down as he chewed his anti-airsickness life-saving peppermints, which, he claimed, have a mysterious effect of antispasmosis and anti-zymosis (relaxing and preventing fermentation of the intestine) which make flying tolerable. My liking for peppermints was simple and unintellectual; having been told, however, why I should take them, I fervently hoped that Toni's faith in their pharmacological action would be justified!

It was getting a little choppy, yet not as bad as I had expected, flying so low at that time of day. Ted was a marvellous and careful pilot; he knew his way like a homing pigeon, exuding confidence, and sharing it with us. He must have known that some time during this, our 'maiden flight', macabre thoughts and remembrances would find their way into our consciousness. He spoke of his love for flying and described the route to keep us occupied, and though I could not hear him too clearly from where I sat, I understood what he was doing and was grateful. As I watched the racing clouds below us I thought of Barrie, wondering whether he, too, was in some breathtakingly beautiful, cloud-touched heaven in the astral world.

I had gone to see a medium just after his death, a direct medium who sat drinking tea with me while she looked into another world. An ordinary, everyday setting for such searchings; no darkness, no mystery. I had gone only because both Toni and I had been worried by a sort of 'presence', a feeling that he had not quite left and that his spirit wished to convey something to us. She saw him clearly with two friends on a beach, happy, content with the reason for his sudden parting, only concerned for the family whom he had left behind. Through the medium he gave me a message and I passed it on, for better or for worse. Had I been right to dabble in the supernatural? I accepted afterlife absolutely, accepted the philosophy of the continuation of life, and of reincarnation on to Earth. Though Barrie was cut off from the life he had loved and had revelled in, projected into another sphere in a matter

46

of hours, he did not seem to grieve or rebel against his Fate. He said, and this was part of his message, that he 'understood why it had happened'. Just that. Acceptance, learnt so quickly! And this had been only two weeks after his passing! Was this not the knowledge we had needed to wipe out the nightmare?

I tapped Toni on the shoulder. 'Feel good?'

'Wonderful,' he replied. 'Really ought to learn to fly.'

The scenery had changed and the cloud ceiling dispersed. Far away, but still visible as a purple mountain barrier, lay the northern frontier. Beyond, though we could not see it, the hot, endless desert. We were losing height. The plains were now dotted with mountains, sudden, uneven projections of the earth, unreal, remote like the backdrop of a dream. Ted pointed to twin peaks straight ahead. 'That's Mugwongo, George's hill, where he has made his camp. He lives on this side, the airstrip is round the back of it. We won't land there— I must check up on things in camp first. Then we'll drive over. Five minutes by air, an hour and a half by road.'

We were losing altitude again and I saw the winding, green-banked river which flows into Leopard Rock Camp, more like a handful of pebbles than the mountain I had expected to find. As Ted circled I saw the baobab trees, grey elephantine shapes, roots towards heaven leaves shed, naked, enigmatic, their cream of tartar fruits (as Ted told me later) delicious fare for the thirsty traveller. At the second circle I saw eland and giraffe quite near the camp, oblivious, hardly favouring us with a second glance. There was a group of five buffalo, two rhinos and a lone bull elephant with whom I would become acquainted later on.

Seeing this magnificence of Nature gave me a small glimpse of what this Sanctuary actually contained, and I understood much better the expression of pride on Ted's face whenever he spoke about Meru. 'Wait and see,' he had said, grinning from ear to ear, his bespectacled eyes lighting up with joy. Well, here it was, the land of his dreams, the Park of his creation.

47

As if in a fairy tale, two half-tame crowned cranes stood like a welcoming committee, awaiting us at the end of the landing strip. I alighted from the plane and stood admiring them, suddenly realizing that I not only felt well, but very hungry. There had simply been no time to feel airsick!

Ted's home was a dreamhouse. Reaching the entrance, rather nondescript and even ugly, we entered through a dark passage expecting a drab, run-of-the-mill bachelor habitation. But like a dark tunnel leading to paradise, it ended in a spacious stone and wood room, sloping down from dining- to living-room to veranda, and farther down still to the steep steps of a lovely garden, inclining to the river and pool below.

The flowing water gave an air of calm beauty. Outside a tropical day of simmering heat; here, a cool oasis quite remote from the world. 'Have you got a mistress hidden somewhere?' I asked our host. 'Surely you didn't dream all this up yourself! It is too perfect for a bachelor, and such a waste!'

Ted showed us the house; neat, tastefully furnished, complete, yet as if waiting to be perfected. This unusual nesting instinct in a game warden could only mean one thing, as he had hinted to us in Nairobi, and one thing alone! I restrained my curiosity and went to change for a swim, feeling slightly guilty when Ted went off to work, even for a short time, while we lazed and splashed in the river pool. I floated on my back and watched the sentry. Not far above us he stood in the shelter of a thatched and stone hut, ever ready, protecting the camp and the Reserve from the 'Shifta', the bandits of the north who had, for years, waged guerrilla warfare for the repossession of land on the Kenya-Somalia border. It should have seemed warlike, uncertain and uncomfortable, but it wasn't. No one here made a fuss about using passwords at night, but nevertheless one had to know them. The menace of attack was always there, but somehow it was still safer than most of the rest of the world. Perhaps the tourist trade suffered, but then the bad road to Meru didn't help much either. What a strange world of contrasts we lived in!

After a quick lunch and some coffee to ward off the sleepiness which comes upon one in near-Equator Africa, we set off for George Adamson's camp. 'It's quite a drive,' Ted warned us, 'and the road is far from good.'

Though he was right, of course, and the road was unbelievably bad, there was so much to see that discomforts mattered very little. Just occasionally, when my legs got almost irretrievably tangled up with the gear-shift lever (far worse for the driver than for me), or when I was pitched against Ted or Toni with too much force, did I become aware of my immediate surroundings. Everything was green and lush, densely treed and shrubbed. To me, this was the epitome of Africa, this was how I had always imagined it would be. We passed oryx, impala, waterbuck and many other antelope, herds of giraffe, duiker diving back into the bush, mongoose scuttling away. Ears, eyes everywhere, often just a flash of brown or grey in the undergrowth. The bird life was fantastic. I wanted to linger but there wasn't time; we still had a long way to go.

Ted drove the Toyota rather as he had flown the plane: with efficient ease. When we approached an impossible-looking culvert, my heart sank, and I had visions of walking mile upon mile for help. Ted took it gently and slowly, easing the bulky vehicle up the steep, rough slope with complete confidence. About halfway between Leopard Rock and Mugwongo there was a plank bridge laid over the plunging Rojowero River which we could hear competing with the sounds of the crickets as we approached. Ted got out and carefully examined it, gauging the stability of the planks at the edges where the river had lapped the sides in a recent storm. I wandered away, following the scent of wild blossom, and found a Doum palm by the bank, its hard fruit, beloved by elephants, shining white like pseudo-ivory, yellow-throated francolins moved away as I approached, but two honey guides found me attractive. Perhaps they were hoping that I would search for honey and that they would get their share of the spoils if they led me to it. The trees were beautiful. It was as if I were standing among ancient monuments of the jungle; huge thorny acacias, the tree that spells Africa for the rest of the world. Fig trees, spreading, enfolding, favourite playground of the baboons. Plovers, swallows, doves lived among them, and behind it all the insect chorus of the forest. Through it I heard a strange but familiar sound: 'Auw, auw', sharp, like the call of a baboon.

Toni was summoning me, and reluctantly I walked back to the plank bridge. 'Could I ride on the roof?' I begged. 'It would be so lovely to get a top view.' I had done this whenever I could, from childhood onwards. Petrol fumes, engine sounds, the rattle of doors, all cancelled out so much of the surroundings. And if these were sheer enchantment, alive with wings and swishing tails, then all the more reason to look at them from above rather than below!

'Certainly not,' Toni said gruffly. 'You get inside.' I was tempted to argue, when Ted joined the discussion.

'There are lions here, not only George's but lots of other very wild ones. There are also leopard. When we reach George's camp his lions may all be at home. You might make them nervous,' he added with a smile, as I climbed into the centre seat.

They really were treating me like a child! Like a wayward child, at that. Then I remembered the elephant we had spotted from the air and decided to acquiesce gracefully. 'You are married now,' Toni said, 'you must learn to do what you are told.'

'It's bliss,' I said, much to the men's surprise, 'just heaven to be bullied. Wait till I start on you!'

'Wise fellow,' Toni said, leaning forward and facing Ted, 'how long till you fall by the wayside?'

'Not too long.' I was delighted, partly for Ted, and partly because my instinct had been right. Ted was probably counting the days of his freedom right now. He wouldn't tell us much, except that the girl he intended to bully would be coming quite soon, that is, provided he could lure her to Meru. When he spoke something soft crept into his voice, something

I had not detected in his eulogies about the Game Reserve. There was no doubt about it at all, Ted was in love.

The approach to George Adamson's camp was a great delight. It finally proves that man's ideas are mostly topsy-turvy and that only very few live the right way about! First we saw the lions, sprawled out in all directions, some almost hidden in the long grass. They hardly gave us a glance as we rattled by, though one (I later learnt he was 'Boy') did finally do us the honour of getting up and staring at us as we passed. I was so absorbed in the lion tribe that the camp and its wire fortifications came as a complete surprise. George had heard us and was standing at the open gate, his assistant, Mike Adam, behind him.

'He is rather like a lion,' I found myself thinking, as he came out to greet us. He was sunburnt, well built, naked to the waist, a white beard softening his face. I had imagined him like this, had seen photographs, yet there was something subtle and forceful, a dynamic quality tempered with sweetness which nothing but the real man could convey.

'How wonderful,' I said to him after Ted had formally introduced us, 'you do have the right idea. The animals are free and you are caged. It's a zoo in reverse!'

'As it should be, and more often,' he said laughing softly, and took us through the make-shift gate into his Mkuti (palm leaf) thatch living-room hut and offered us tea. 'This fence wasn't actually built for the sake of a principle though,' he said. 'I built it because when I first came here there were quite a lot of difficulties that had to be ironed out. The wild lions came into my tent, which was rather inconvenient, and I had to find a way to stop them.'

'Master of understatement,' I thought, 'how like a man of his calibre to play it down.' I urged him to tell us what had happened.

'It was actually Ugas, who is now in such trouble with his eye, who started it all.' George filled his pipe, lit it and pulled at it.

Although there was work to be done and the hours were

passing, I could have gladly sat in the hazy early afternoon for ever listening to the stories that George had to tell.

'When I first made this camp, almost two years ago, I brought Ugas with me, and Boy and Girl, who were only cubs. There were plenty of wild lions whose land this was, quite apart from all the other inhabitants, like elephant, who were not in the least disturbed by lion as long as they were left alone. Ugas had to fight to establish his territory. Adjustments have to be made in any society like this.'

He smiled, remembering his first days of trial and tribulation, and offered us more tea.

The trials were, and had been, his as much as the lions'. Bwana Simba, the lion-man! Perhaps there never had been or never would be such a man again. Not a recluse, not an eccentric, but one who was willing to share his experiences and his love of the wild, yet who belonged so much more to the wild than to the kingdom of man.

'Even now, after this long time,' George continued, 'you can hear my lions and the wild lions roaring at each other in the night. It is the most awesome sound. There were fierce fights in those days. Ugas, leader of the pride, not used or expert at defending himself, was chased back into camp by a wild lion one night. He dived under my bed and the other lion after him, and I had the devil's own job to sort it out.'

He took a puff at his pipe. 'So you see what I mean,' he said, looking at me. 'It's safer this way, though Girl jumps over the fence quite often. But she is the only one.'

Then George told us about Ugas's injury; he didn't know for certain what had caused it but thought it might have been a spitting snake, or perhaps a fight with a wild lion who scratched the eye. He got up to call Ugas, and we followed, watching him walk into the long grass at the back of the camp. Ugas, though invisible to us, wasn't very far away and responded almost at once, lured by nothing but the voice of his human friend. Gentle, evenly insistent, coaxing. 'OOOgas,' he called, pitching his voice in such a way that it sounded like the call of a lion, 'Come on, Oogas, poor old OOgas.' He called over and over again until the lion appeared, walked straight over to him, leaned on him and purred loudly. It was the most amazing sight I had ever seen.

'He isn't quite as good-tempered as usual,' George said, stroking his mane. 'The eye must be very painful. It would be best for you to approach carefully and slowly. No sudden movements.' He then suggested that we first drive the Land-Rover a little nearer to him and look at the eye from there. Then Toni should approach. As Ugas was little used to women, I should stay in the car until George told me to come. He was taking every precaution and being almost apologetic about it.

Boy and Girl, then just over two years old, weren't very far away either. They never were when one wanted them to be. They must have known there was something in the air and were determined to find out all they could about it. In spite of George's threats and attempts to drive them away, they were not to be budged. They acted like children who wanted to be part of the fun.

They had both appeared in the film, *Born Free*, and had taken a vital part in the re-enactment of the Elsa story. George had managed to keep them as well as Ugas, who had also played a very important role and whom George had trained. 'Ugas' means 'Prince' in the Somali language. He looked like one. Long and dark-maned, he stood very high next to George, who estimated him as weighing over 400 pounds. He really did look royal, even with his opaque suppurating eye. George had brought him from the orphanage of the Nairobi National Park where he had been put after the filming was over and where he was thought to be fierce and unreliable. I was told that George, having got permission to bring him to Meru for re-habilitation, drove to the orphanage, backed his Land-Rover against the gate of Ugas's enclosure, opened it and called the lion, whereupon he happily jumped up into the back and was taken to his new home. When first I heard this story I believed only a small part of it. But now, seeing the two together, the huge lion and the man, it was easy to understand that it had happened in just such a way.

53

The eye looked terrible. George was steadying the head with one hand and holding the jaws against his own body with the other. After Toni's first approach, during which Ugas lifted his great head and appraised him with his good eye for a long minute, George signalled me to come, and we were able to see that the damage was of some months' standing and would be difficult to repair. While we looked and felt the edge of the eye, George kept up his soothing refrain. 'All right, Oogas, poor Oogas,' he repeated hypnotically, and again I had the impression that his voice was a lion's soft grunt, the sound one sometimes hears when a lion is very near. Our patient's restlessness disappeared and he allowed himself to be held firmly. I wanted to use our magnifying glass and needed a very steady hand; there was just a suspicion that a thorn or piece of wood might have entered the eye or the eyelid. Slowly we instilled some local ophthalmic anaesthetic mixture into the eye and waited. Ugas was very patient. It would be a great relief to his aching eye when the drops took effect and deadened the pain.

Meanwhile Boy and Girl had settled down to watch us from a more useful and respectful distance, a great relief for we needed all hands on deck. Their stomachs were bulging and they had obviously decided to sleep it off. At this stage of rehabilitation George was still feeding them once or twice a week, getting his meat by shooting outside the boundary of the Reserve. Slowly, all three lions were becoming more and more independent and able to kill for themselves, while George was able to keep an eye on his trio, making a careful study of their habits, the growth rate of the younger two, and their social behaviour. At first they had come into camp at regular intervals, but soon they stayed away for longer and longer periods, even from the temptation of a sumptuous meal. At such times he would go out to search for them on foot, be it day or night, armed with a torch and nothing else but his great courage, his love and a marvellous 'bush' sense of direction. If there had been leonine sounds of war in the vicinity, he would go at once to investigate, for the indigenous lions were

54

still hostile and slow to relinquish their territory. I have heard him tell some hair-raising stories of what he found and how he managed to step in and rescue his charges. What he never did tell was how often and how narrowly he must have escaped injury, perhaps as I once suggested to him, through the continued watchful eye of not one but a host of guardian angels, who had very little time to rest between episodes.

Many people disagreed with what he was doing. We respected their opinions, agreed that much of what they said made sense, but advised them to go and see for themselves before coming to any definite conclusion. Their main contention was that these lions, then only three in number but later nine, were being interfered with too much, that their return to freedom was a farce. More than that, that it was a dangerous venture since half-tame lions in a Game Reserve could only lead to tragedy. Everyone admired George Adamson, yet his admirers simply would not give him the benefit of the doubt. They thought his project sentimental, ill-advised and a waste of time.

There were also those few of us who believed in him and the more Toni and I worked with him the better we understood what it was all about. It had to have a beginning, a basic plan which would progress as slowly as Nature itself dictated: the temperament of the lions being released, their ability to find new territory and their own food; the strength of their hunting instincts hitherto suppressed, their health and response to the new environment and their pride consciousness, for their only real chance was as a group; lately, their sexual virility and their urge to mate with their wild counterparts. All these factors and developments George watched with the eye of an observer who was so involved that he seemed to become part of the pride. Progress may have seemed slow, and there were setbacks. Ugas's eye injury was one, later a cub was killed by a wild lion. The unsympathetic public were waiting for these, holding them up as reasons to discontinue. Yet Meru, which only later became a National Park, was still a remote, not much frequented wildlife sanctuary and there would be years, years precious to George Adamson, in which to succeed if only he was left in peace!

We were proud to be part of his experiment which contained as much of the pioneering spirit as a flight into space, or a new surgical technique. When, in the history of the world, has there ever been an attempt into the unknown without injury, without sacrifice? One had only to be with George and his lions, sense and see their unique relationship, unemotional, normal, a sort of man-to-man understanding which in itself broke the barriers of previous animal-man communication; when one witnessed this first hand, then there were no more questions to ask. The tourist would be satisfied to keep away from a lion, which would probably be marked in some way when the need arose; he would be proud to be asked to be part of the experiment by, perhaps, plotting the lions' position on a special map of the Sanctuary. There might be a biologist helping to record it all on a more strictly scientific basis, laying the foundation for new knowledge which in turn would bring lions in Africa closer to survival. They, after some years (as actually did happen), would merge with the wild, surviving completely without bonus square meals and medical attention. It was a labour of humility, patience and understanding. George Adamson had been blessed with all three; the world could learn much from his example!

While waiting for the eye-drops to take effect, we discussed out patient, now leaning affectionately on his friend, and all aspects of his injury. Previous and unsuccessful treatment had been given and this made the prognosis all the more uncertain. George was anxious that Ugas should not undergo prolonged suffering, preferring radical treatment, which meant complete removal of the eye. We felt that this would be the last resort, and that we would prefer him to have one more chance of treatment if possible.

True, he was pawing at the eye which retarded healing in any case, but if we could leave eye-drops containing an anaesthetic as well as the ointment, it might well stop the painful irritation which caused the vicious circle: injury in the first place, infection, pain, interference of the wound causing new damage. I had never treated a lion before, but this type of wound, where bandaging or restraint was not possible, where only tranquillizers would arrest self-injury, was common both in felines and canines. I had had excellent results if the client was prepared to instil ointment or drops into the eye every four hours, the only way to get tissue response. This and collateral therapy, such as injections, might well cause recovery in a relatively short time. Finally, as Ugas would not allow the eyelid to be touched, we administered a tranquillizer as well and found that there was no thorn or foreign body anywhere, but only a longstanding infection, a very cloudy cornea and ulceration to one side which could have been caused by many things.

It was easy to treat him when he was tranquillized. The question was, would Ugas allow George to inject him while untranquillized, and for how long, how often? For how long would the huge bulk of 400-pound lion be patient and understanding? We had taken the precaution of bringing antibiotics which were almost painless. Almost—but not quite, for there always is some pressure into the tissues as the liquid infiltrates and reaches the sensory nerve endings. Thick suspensions, sometimes more efficient and long-acting in their effect, were out of the question here. Apart from the danger, there was the pain.

It could be agonizing. I had developed sympathy for my patients the hard way years before, when a very good doctor friend of mine had cause to treat me with one of those broth-like injections. 'I want something strong and effective,' I had told him. 'I must be at work. I can't let a simple case of tonsillitis interfere with my practice.'

'All right, you asked for it,' he had said, and injected me posteriorly (since I would not be needing that part of me in practice) with the speed of lightning. For a full twenty minutes afterwards I hopped up and down in misery and pain, sparing no curses and grinding my teeth in between. I had a queue of clients waiting in my own surgery but could hardly return to

57

them gripping my backside. I had no alternative but to remain where I was and listen to the sympathy of my medical colleague. 'Now you know how it feels, sweetheart,' he said with a grin. 'I bet a cow's bottom has just as many nerve-endings as yours.'

A cow's bottom indeed! I limped back to my rooms, insult heaped upon pain, yet for ever afterwards paid special attention to the material I injected, adding local anaesthetic to my syringe whenever there was need.

We left a stock of medicine for George to use and begged him to be very careful. Pfizer Veterinary Division in Nairobi had most kindly given me a number of their products which I thought I might need and which indeed we did. We decided to give the eye one more chance and this would entail keeping in touch by radio-telephone and judging the situation according to progress—or otherwise. We would return to Meru if necessary, and take a look at the eye again the next day before leaving for Nairobi.

Having left Ugas in the grass outside the fence, slightly whoozy but not 'out for the count', we returned to the centre hut for some rehydrating tea before leaving for Leopard Rock. The black-headed weavers, seemingly unaffected by the burning sun, were busily building and repairing their fantastic nest-empire, their tree an enormous acacia which towered over the whole camp. I could see them from where I sat, fascinated by their unending display of energy. They were weaving newly gathered grass-threads in and out, out and in, making a solid, wind and rainproof structure with architectural precision. Did the parents teach the young, or was this pattern of skill woven into their genes, as some thought, for generations and generations? Would a bird be rehabilitated more swiftly into the wild than a lion because its personality would accept the human touch and influence less readily in the first place? I would have liked to have stayed much longer, watching the weavers above, and the lions below, waiting for the sun to sink and the stars to rise, listening to the lions challenging each other. Perhaps another time. I took a last look at the dozing Ugas and climbed into the Toyota. George, standing next to his patient, waved us good-bye and thanked us, then turned to the reclining head and fondled it, part of Africa even as the lion was the symbol of Africa. As I turned back to catch a glimpse of them, they had merged in the sunlight, golden mane and white beard quite indistinguishable.

4 Almost a Meal

PERHAPS I HAD been dreaming about a lion-hunt in reverse, for I remember the terrifying sensation of something powerfully animal closing in on me. I was losing ground, inch by inch, then everything went black and I went crashing into an abyss. I started out of sleep—what sweet relief—only to hear a chorus of discordant cries above me. I sat up, numb and cold, listening. The nightmare receded. I remembered the welcoming committee of crowned cranes on the airstrip, and Ted's warning that they might wake us when they landed on the roof. Had they begun my dream, or ended it?

I looked at Toni. He was blissfully asleep, quite unaware of my tortures. How boyish he looked, legs curled up in foetal position, hair ruffled and uncombed, features relaxed, unstressed, the restless tenseness and burning energy of his waking hours quite dispelled. He certainly wasn't being hunted, unless his high-bosomed pin-up, Sophia Loren, was hot on his track! But that could only be heaven for him, I reflected, now *very* wide awake! As long as he keeps her for his dreams or on the film screen, I really couldn't object, especially as he always insisted that he loved her only because she looked like me, even if my vital statistics were somewhat different!

Dawn was already filtering through the window and would not linger long. Great pity that the sky would not stay gentle-pink in tropical Africa. Almost as soon as one looked up at the newness and the beauty, it was gone, passed into full day. I thought of the sleepy cities where morning is an after-coffee affair, where day and night are created by office hours and hangovers and curtains drawn to keep out the brightness of the sunlight. Here, in Meru, life had to adjust itself to the rhythm of the wild which had no artificial sun or alarm-clocks. Up with dawn, down not too long after dark.

Toni did not altogether agree with my thoughts on the subject or share my enthusiasm for early morning starts. He hardly registered until he had eaten breakfast and there was no doubt at all that it was dangerous to approach him with anything but breakfast at such a time.

'Do wake up!' After all, we were away from the city now and it was a lovely day. I shook him gently, and when that made no impression I began to kiss his nose, then tweaked it until he tried to swat me away as if I were a mosquito.

'Barbarous,' he murmured, 'what time is it?'

'Swimming time,' I said, half pulling him out of bed with a huge effort. 'You must come and swim before breakfast.' At that point the cook brought tea and saved the day. Toni loved early tea, especially in someone else's house since at home we only drank 'morning' lemon-water. He only half believed that I was trying to save his liver from caffeine poisoning; yet, five tea sessions a day with four cups at least at each inning, plus plenty of coffee, was bound to damage even a Herculean liver. Besides, a liverish man is very hard to live with, especially one who could wave away just about anything with long, confusing, scientific jargon!

'You're younger than I am and you have so much more energy,' he complained, his eyes barely open, but the sound of the rattling teacups had done the trick. It was no use telling him at this hour that he hadn't reached middle age yet, that, in fact, he never would if he constantly missed the dawn, and that men never grew up while women *had* to stay young at any age to survive the trials of living with a man!

'There is a crocodile in the pool; don't you think it might mistake you for a juicy titbit?' Toni was still trying to find a reason for avoiding cold river water, but from the tone of his voice I knew I had won. It was, after all, only a young crocodile, though not many months later it had suddenly grown to formidable size. On that occasion we had been flown up to help Joy Adamson with one of her cheetah cubs. The pilot, returning to collect us the next afternoon, could not be persuaded to join us in the rock-pool. He had patiently waited on top of the steps until we appeared dripping wet, exhilarated by the cold water. I had laughingly told him about the crocodile. 'We swim with it,' I joked, 'but it doesn't mind.'

'Is that the one?' he had said, rising to his feet, pointing down to the river separated from the pool by a stone dam. And there to our horror, lying in the shallows, was a very large croc, half hidden in the side of the bank. But that had been later, and perhaps it wasn't the same resident crocodile, but just an innocuous passer-by!

'Just splash around if it worries you,' Ted had said on the previous night. But that morning, as we lay half submerged on the rocks, watching the pink light turn into the yellow of another Meru day, there had been no crocodile. Ted had left long before to organize the building of pens for his rhino. He was leaving for South Africa within three weeks to organize their transport and had to be everywhere at once. A location away from swampland had to be found so that the challenge of the tse-tse fly would be less of a hazard for the newcomers. He was supervising the building of much-needed roads, had to attend to matters concerning the camp and tourists, keep an eye on the guards, control poaching and see to the welfare of all his employees. He had some help but not much. His was a marathon task already; the reintroduction of three pairs of square-lipped rhinoceros was a full-time hobby. I hoped that his wife-to-be would be able to help him and become used to his long absences from camp. It was not only a warden who had to be utterly devoted, enduring and eternally optimistic, but it was the warden's wife who had to possess all these qualities—and more. Ted was lucky he had found a woman who would share all his burdens, though how great these were to be, even he could never have guessed.

'Breakfast!' Ted had returned and we climbed out of the

pool and up the flower-bedecked slope under the watchful eyes of the guard, and went to change. The slate-grey nightmare cranes, having successfully woken me, had descended to ground-level and were feeding, their golden crests glistening in the sunlight.

We couldn't dawdle over our meal that morning, for Ted was anxious to fly off to Mugwongo before it became too hot. From there, when our work with Ugas was finished, he would fly us straight back to Nairobi and then return to Meru again. It was hard to plan the day for the unexpected always occurred, here even more than in the hour-ridden world to which we would have to return before the sun was down. This time we had no misgivings about our flight, but were eager to get up so we could look down. I had barely begun to look for animals when it was time to land, five minutes south-west of Leopard Rock. Ted circled low and buzzed George's camp. The Land-Rover was parked inside the fence but there was little sign of life. We reached the airstrip in a moment and prepared to land when I saw that it was occupied already and that the occupants were firmly established in direct line with our descent. My heart missed a beat or two, and I looked at Ted. The zebra and eland were feeding at the edge of the strip as we approached, flying low to alarm them, yet unable to touch down. I thought they would scatter at the sound of the revving engine, but they only moved a short distance away. By the time Ted had circled again, prepared to land, they had returned. Once more Ted made an arch away from the twin peaks, turned and banked. This time the trespassers took the hint: the zebra galloped off at speed, the eland trotted off heads high, aristocrats of all antelope, even in flight.

The Land-Rover arrived soon afterwards, but George wasn't driving. Aaron Sharma, George's junior assistant, had come with a scout to protect the plane from hyena, the most undiscriminating, omnivorous scavenger, who, among other things, had been known to enjoy the wings of an aeroplane! We transferred our medical kit once more and drove along the curving, rocky path to the camp, which, though very near, could not be reached in a hurry if the Land-Rover's suspension was to be preserved. Driving in George's vehicle brought the atmosphere of his lions very close indeed. The odour with which they had impregnated the vehicle was not unpleasant. It was distinctly wild and very strong, quite unlike the scent of lions I remembered in the zoo. I idly wondered, as the Land-Rover came to a shuddering halt at the edge of camp, whether the human smell made such a definite impression upon the lions, travelling as they often did in a man-impregnated vehicle.

George, Aaron told us, was out looking for Girl who had not returned with the other two at dawn. There had been a great deal of roaring that night from the direction of the hill and George was worried since Girl was rather young to fend for herself. She was, after all, an adolescent lioness who had not yet acquired the *savoir faire* of the wild, especially with regard to sex. She reached maturity at the age of two years and eight months, some time before Boy, her litter mate. Even then, having successfully mated with a wild lion and produced cubs, she was not an exemplary mother, as often happens with the first litter of any animal. It was, however, a great stride forward, for merging with the wild was what George had hoped would happen. In November of that year he wrote to us, rather wryly I thought, on the subject, including some anecdotes on the love-life and struggles of his beloved lions:

Girl gave birth to two male cubs on the 25th Oct., on top of Mugwongo Hill where she kept them for nearly a month, changing the hiding places frequently. Then one morning, I found her close to camp with one cub only. Spent four days looking for the missing one but never found a trace of it. Almost certainly it was taken by a leopard. Probably while Girl was carrying the one and before she had time to fetch the other. She is not a very good mother, often leaving the surviving cub for a whole day or night. Now her milk appears to have almost dried up and I have to bottle feed the infant.

Ugas and Boy now spend most of their time chasing after

Ugas's eye looked terrible

The elephant was not disturbed by Girl

George Adamson helps the author remove stitches from Ugas's eye

wild lionesses, with considerable success although not without some hard knocks. A few mornings ago Ugas limped home looking very sorry for himself, a paw bitten through and a nasty gash under one ear, the result of a fight with a wild male, over some female I expect.

Then I found Boy in the company of a real old pro with a battle-scarred face and an ear chewed off!! One day Ugas and Boy had a real set-to, standing on their hind legs swiping each other with both paws and claws extended. Any one of the clouts could have removed half the face of a human, but there was little or no damage. Finally, it was Ugas who gave way. What trouble the fair sex can cause!?

We decided to while away the time waiting for George, with a pot of George's best home-brew and sat down in the rustic hut lined with bookshelves on one side, cutlery and some canned foods stacked on the other, and at the entrance his desk, typewriter at the ready, letters, files and films scattered everywhere in true male fashion. George was writing a book about his life and work, one that would be sincere and down to earth; the story of his unique adventure-filled years in Africa. It was a wonderful thought that he was at last committing himself to paper, for there was much that he could not, and would never tell in any other way. He grumbled, as we all do, about the time and effort it took him. Yet here, in the middle of nowhere, was the perfect setting for an author. I wished I could join him for a few months—but that could never be while I had my own tribe of young—and old—to take care of.

While the others were setting the world to rights, I went to see if I could find Ugas. I passed under the weaver colony beyond the big sleeping tent and stood at the gate, searching the long grass, low trees and bushes for any sign of lion. I had always admired people with 'bush eyes' who could detect the slightest movement or shape or colour variation in a sea of greens and browns. I had passed the 'every ant-heap a lion' stage, but still had great difficulty in discovering the signs which meant that something other than grass was hidden in the grass. I stood quite still and tried to acclimatize to my surroundings. There was so much out there beyond the fence, even in one acre of wild land, and what a numbskull I was to be aware of so little of it!

A low thorn tree grew to the left and in front of where I stood, and in its shade I found Ugas. I glimpsed him just as I was about to return to the others; sprawled, as lions do, in every possible direction at once, the classic posture of feline abandonment. I went back to the hut, took someone's binoculars off the back of a chair and returned. I was very anxious to see how Ugas's eye was and thought that this would be as good a time as any to conduct a preliminary examination of our patient. But Ugas was dozing and didn't care to be examined. I called his name but he didn't stir, not even one inch. Either his dreams were more powerful than my voice, or else he didn't deign to be associated with me. He looked so quiet, so good-natured, and so relaxed that I decided to take one or two steps towards him to catch his attention and get him to lift his head.

To do that I had to open the wire gate. There was no one in sight to advise me one way or the other, so I followed my inclination, and my impatience, and went through, just a few steps away from camp. I only wanted to rouse Ugas sufficiently to gain his attention; then he could go back to sleep. I moved forward very slowly, binoculars at the ready, thinking that he might just look up for a moment to find out what was rustling the grass. But he didn't. I moved farther, about ten more steps towards the lion's tree. Then I stopped again, and called very softly: 'Ooogas, Oogas.' He sat up then, and in the split second that I first saw his eyes I sensed danger and knew that I had been a fool to leave the safety of the camp. He glared at me, all alertness; one moment asleep, and in the next he had leapt towards me with a growl, covering the distance with a few bounds. I remember only one conscious thought: 'That's it. Nothing will stop him and it's my own fault,' and I remember that I was sweating with fear.

66

My instinct was to turn and run—stupidity itself—yet my self-control had never been schooled to such an emergency. I knew I must stand my ground yet my limbs already made a movement towards the fence, the completion of which might well have cost me my life. But I did not complete it; a voice reached out to me from behind at the critical moment.

'Stay where you are. Don't move. Keep looking at him.'

Mike Adam had somehow appeared; he knew Ugas and realized that rushing out to help me might have the opposite effect. 'Thank the good Lord he is alone,' I thought, for I knew that if Toni had been there nothing on earth could have stopped him from taking violent action, and that might have made matters much worse.

With my heart literally beating in my mouth, knowing that Ugas must be picking up the scent of fear, I stood my ground, encouraged and fortified by Mike's steely voice behind me. I looked Ugas straight in the eye and spoke to him. His body, still arched from the leap, now relaxed, and he stared back at me, summing me up, his good dark yellow eye wild and unpredictable, giving as yet no indication of his feelings towards me. I continued to speak to him soothingly, at the same time attempting to control the hammering in my throat. I tried to exclude all thought except that we were friends and to send him calming vibrations. His tail was swishing from side to side as he half crouched in front of me, but I noticed with relief that his ears were not laid back. After some time, which seemed for ever (but lasted only a few minutes), he gave a grunt and leaned his whole body against me, purring loudly as he playfully pawed my leg, his claws partly sheathed.

'Move back slowly now,' Mike said. 'Keep looking at him; I'll come out and try to distract him.'

Ugas's attention was now partly on me and partly on Mike who approached from behind. Regaining confidence, I looked down at his bad eye and saw that the discharge looked less purulent. I began to stroke his mane and ease away from the weight of his body and as I did so he turned and moved towards Mike, who was calling him.

Gradually I retreated, step by step as instructed, and by the time Ugas had returned to the shade of the tree I had reached the fence. Ted and Toni were looking at me rather strangely as I walked through the gate, my legs about to buckle at the knees. Neither of them said anything at first. They must have known what had happened, judging from their expressions! Toni looked just as I remember feeling when a horse had stepped on my toe and moved on—a little shocked with pain, and intensely grateful that it was over. By the time we reached the tea-house, George had returned. He had found Girl, and she had come back with him, all in one piece and very hungry.

I decided to tell him there and then of my incredible folly; nothing ever seemed quite so dreadful when told over a cup of strong tea! George gave me a sidelong glance of horror mingled with disappointment and stroked his beard. I waited for his comment with trepidation, knowing he would be as kind as he could, though I deserved severe reprimand.

At last, after some moments of deep thought, he spoke. His tone was not scolding or reprimanding as it might have been, but kindly, just as if he were explaining a difficult problem to a backward child. 'A lion,' he said, after lighting his pipe, 'always keeps his instincts. It doesn't matter whether he is tame, half tame or wild, it doesn't matter where or how he has been raised. I don't say he always does, but he may. If he knocks someone down, especially a stranger, then that man—or woman,' he looked at me meaningfully, his overhanging thick eyebrows making him look suddenly very stern, 'is just so much meat. Just a meal.'

Seeing my look of penitence, he stopped. Perhaps he had expected me to remonstrate, to make excuses for my behaviour; nothing was further from my thoughts. 'If Ugas had knocked you down he would have been following the normal pattern of lion behaviour. It would have been so quick that I doubt that Mike could have helped you. It was a good thing, though, that he was there. If you had turned your back and run, Ugas might have flattened you with a swipe of his paw.'

Toni had been listening intently and now firmly took my

hand in his. 'I have always said it, and I shall say it again!' He spoke slowly and a little louder than usual, as if trying to hide his true feelings. '*I must never let you out of my sight.* You just cannot cope without me!' His remark broke the tension and we laughed heartily.

'I usually argue with him but today I haven't a leg to stand on,' I said. 'Chalk it up,' I added, 'that's one up to you to prove how right you really always are.'

I had done some pretty stupid things in my life especially during the course of my veterinary career. I had taken quite unnecessary chances when the slow, safe way was just as good. And yet, having promised myself that wisdom comes with maturity, I had done it again, taken a chance which could have ended in disaster. Had I been injured or worse, it would have proved to those who opposed George's work that they were right just at a time when, in fact, they were beginning to be proved wrong. Perhaps this would sink in, and teach me the lesson I needed, with Toni to help every inch of the way!

5 *Operation Ugas*

TONI WAS NOT a man to gloat over one's mistakes, yet the day in George's camp when I had so nearly upset the applecart seemed to prey on his mind.

'You need a holiday, a change from the city.' He regarded me more thoughtfully, less absent-mindedly than usual, and I had guessed his thoughts. Only a very overtired, overwrought female could have committed such an idiocy! I knew he was giving me the benefit of the doubt, making overwork, fatigue associated with settling into new surroundings, the reason for my lack of judgement. That was kind of him and I was grateful. There was no doubt about it at all, if we had both needed a tonic and a rest before, it had now become clear that getting away from Nairobi as soon as possible was of prime importance.

In a way the city engulfed us less than many, for our home, rented from the University College where Toni worked, was set on the slope of a hill, with the result that wailing sirens and screaming engines were muffled, sometimes even muted. When the wind blew the right way the constant flow of traffic took on a murmur reminiscent of waves upon the shore, inducing a state of acute sea nostalgia. Our neighbours were hidden by tall trees and thick scrub, thus saving us from the roof-top over-each-hedge encroachment associated with life in suburbia. They were kindly, generous people, the sort from whom one could, without hesitation, borrow anything at a moment's notice. They felt a constant guilt owing to the sounds emanating from their boat-building activities which only just balanced the din of our often chaotic household. What, after all, could be more soothing and at times stirring, than the crackle of electric welding or the beating of metal, especially when the result was a beautiful, twelve-ton, seaworthy mariner's dream?

'If we don't get away soon I will do something worse.' I knew a dire threat was needed to make Toni take action and plan a holiday, for within three days of our return from Meru he had, once more, become engulfed in the piles of letters upon his desk. Unlike many others, whose sole task it was to teach and to organize a college department, his leisure hours were filled with his 'hobby', as a result of which he was inundated with mail concerning his wildlife work. My threat paid dividends, for within two days we set out to visit our only relative in East Africa, Toni's amazing medical-missionary sister, Lenie, and her recently acquired family, in Entebbe, Uganda.

The children had gone south to the family, and we should have felt free, released from all worry and obligations, able to live the haphazard, blissful sort of existence which gives respite from daily routine. But it wasn't quite like that on this occasion; through Christmas, through family festivities, through our journey to some of the most spectacular of Uganda's National Parks, we felt uneasy, almost eager to return.

When we discussed the cause of our unrest, it became easier, for worry always becomes less as soon as it is shared. What was George doing up there, north-east of the mountain? Was he still able to inject his lion, or had caution persuaded him that such injections were a constant threat to his life? We knew that he would continue at risk to himself for as long as possible, yet he had promised me, on that last radio call before we had left, that he WOULD be careful and dose Ugas by mouth if necessary, even though he knew this method to be less effective. 'He *is* rather growling at me,' he had admitted, and had later confessed that Ugas had once gripped his arm between his teeth as he had felt the needle prick, but had, at the last moment, relaxed his huge jaws which could have crushed his arm to a pulp.

71

By New Year, just after our return, we had received a letter from Meru which did not bear good tidings. Ugas's eye had not maintained progress—but, at least, George was safe! Toni flew up shortly afterwards and prescribed a new line of treatment, for removal of the eye would be the very last resort. Although our views did not agree with those of the anti-rehabilitationists, we did have our own private doubts as to what would happen to Ugas if he were left only with one eye. In a territory so hotly contested by other leonine inhabitants, where an uneasy peace was only now beginning to be observed, would he not be under a severe disadvantage if only one eye remained? Again, as the news somehow leaked out that Ugas's eye was getting worse, a great many opinions were voiced from one end of Kenya to the other. A lion, they insisted, could *never* survive in a one-eyed condition, even if he was completely wild. A half-wild creature, its instincts and aggressive capabilities not fully developed, had no chance at all. He had to be put out of his misery. Dire predictions, even threats of repercussion were heaped upon our heads. If we were part of such wilful cruelty we could expect a fair share of the blame!

By the time Ted's radio call came through, we were so angered by the ignorant pronouncements of people who knew nothing whatsoever about lion behaviour, we had decided that we would do whatever was required of us, but would not, under any circumstance, suggest destruction. We gathered from the message, distorted though it was, that Ugas was in terrible pain, that he had injured himself and would we come at once, or even sooner. We only surmised that the eye was the cause of the emergency, but since time was so precious did not want to wait to place a call to ascertain the exact site of injury. Besides, the radio call channel to Meru was only open at a certain morning hour, by which time, on the next day, we hoped to be well on the way. Unfortunately we could not drop everything at that very moment and just fly up any more than Ted had apparently not been able to come down to fetch us. The children had to be deposited with our good friends, the Schaffer family, who already had six of their own—plus various animals—yet who hardly noticed the advent of another two. Toni, who had his many duties and lectures at the veterinary faculty, had to make arrangements for someone to take over for him. I had to cancel a Hatha Yoga class which meant notifying about twenty pupils and to beg the director of the United Nations Institute where I was teaching veterinary subjects, to excuse me for yet another emergency. He had already threatened to sack me several times. Since Freedom from Hunger was the symbol of his organization, he could not be very sympathetic and for ever tolerant of wildlife ventures which seemed far removed from dry meat products and milk powder.

After this basic planning had been achieved, we had to get down to the business in hand and, once again, put together our instruments and drugs, adding some extra ones in case something other than just an eye needed attention. An aeroplane had to be hired, which was done by the Elsa Trust office in Nairobi, and some toothbrushes and a change of clothes thrown into the overnight bag. George would be needing some supplies, Ted and his new wife would not be able to put us up too easily if we did not bring some of our own special items of diet. Last, but not least, we had to consult our diaries and cancel any social arrangements we had made for the time we would be away, and make sure that the stock of food for our own animals was adequate. Our two maids, Jenny and Maria, always rose to the occasion of such sudden comings and goings most wonderfully, knowing full well that our urges to leave the house and home were not entirely frivolous. Had Toni not taken the trouble to inform them in his classic Kiswahili, where we were going and why, they would still have guessed quite a lot from the blood- and earth-stained, wild animal-scented clothes which we pitched into the laundry basket on our return. 'Tutaenda kuona Bwana Simba' (we are going to see 'Mr. Lion', the typical Swahili custom of naming a man by occupation or association), we said, as we bid them farewell and then I would explain by a series of wing gestures that we would go by air and not by road.

73

'Kwa herini' (good-bye), they would call after us, smiling and waving, concerned for our well-being, yet glad to have some respite from their daily and exacting duties.

An arrangement had been made that we would fly to Mugwongo direct and would be fetched by Ted Goss at sun-down. As we could not take off until after lunch it would be unlikely that anything major could be done until early the next morning. Evening operations, unless absolutely unavoidable, were most ill-advised, especially with a lion who might have a full stomach at the time. Our pilot, though a very nice young man, had forgotten to take his bearings before leaving, thus making our flight, yet once again, something of a trial. So far only Ted Goss had inspired us with a feeling of confidence, the only man who really seemed to know where he was going.

Once we had reached the environs of Meru he had flown very low to find the road into the Reserve, had followed it to the gate, then to the headquarters and so to George's camp by way of the river and the very distinct twin peaks of Mug-wongo itself. George was anxiously awaiting us as we touched down. In that stillness of the after midday haze he must have heard the drone of the Skyhawk engine and wondered why we were so long reaching the landing strip. We unloaded into his Land-Rover and the pilot turned about and flew back to Nairobi, having agreed that he would return to Leopard Rock the next afternoon to take back one or both of us, depending on the condition of our patient.

This time, with George giving us a brief but vivid case history of the past twenty-four hours, we arrived in camp twice as quickly as on the previous occasion when Aaron Sharma, George's assistant, had taken his time to wind his way along the little used, rocky track. Ugas had apparently run his eye into a thorn or sharp stick and had been discovered on the hill near camp, roaring with pain. We could imagine the acute suffering, not only of the lion but of the 'lion man', prompting his immediate decision that something had to be done, even before veterinary help could be obtained. He had injected Ugas with the sedative solution we had left behind in case of emergency, and this had staved off the worst agonies which follow such injury. He had, in fact, shown a wonderful presence of mind at a time when many might have faltered and failed. I had discovered this so often among my most courageous and resourceful clients: they could rise to almost any occasion which did not involve them too closely, too emotionally. As soon as something arose which touched them deeply or shocked them profoundly, their practical common sense and ability to apply their knowledge faded completely. From muscular, tough farmers to 'horsey' women, to medical practitioners, everything failed when personal feelings predominated.

We found Ugas at the back of the camp outside the fence. He was still sleepy from the previous day's injection, and lay head on paws, emitting a low moan as George approached. His eye was a terrible sight. It was swollen and seemed to be filled with a clot of blood which protruded from the surface. At the site of the injury there was distention and bulging of the cornea. We noticed that, though the sun was hot and bright, there was no light response, and he made no attempt to close the lids. While we examined him more closely George soothed the lion with his voice, his face a mixture of acute pain and iron self-control, aware that he would have to summon all his strength to help us on the following morning. There was no doubt about it at all: the eye, his right one, would have to be removed and the operation would have to be performed the next morning. Apart from the pain, the other eye could become affected with resulting blindness if there were too much delay, and that *would* mean the end of Ugas.

After checking his temperature in case of secondary infection, we gave an antibiotic and left instructions that he was under no circumstances to receive any food or to be allowed to leave camp. As soon as the sedation wore off or Ugas showed signs of restlessness, he was to receive yet another dose of Sernylan. We knew full well that, sick and sore though he was, it would take only the roaring of a competitive male to set him bounding out of camp.

'You do realize that there is a fair anaesthetic risk?' I

thought it better to warn George now so that he would be ready to face whatever was to be.

He nodded mutely and smiled a broken-hearted sort of smile of resignation that brought a lump to my throat. 'It's his only chance, and I know you will do your best. To know that is quite enough,' he added as he turned away, his eyes beginning to show his innermost feelings. It was just as well that Ted Goss arrived about that time, for I felt that George would now want to be left alone with his thoughts and with his beloved lion. As we drove away and he turned his back towards camp it struck me that I was not the only wife who took second place: George's affection for Ugas was greater, even, than Toni's veneration of the elephants.

That night we stayed with Ted and his new wife Else and there we determined our plan of operations. We had already thought that Ted's choice of wife was quite superlative. He had somehow imported a Danish girl endowed not only with a lovely face and figure but also with an unusual sensitivity and perception and a great deal of courage. She had left the sophisticated, stimulating, jet-propelled, cosmopolitan society where life is a mixture of exacting service—for she had been an air hostess—and complete relaxation. Here, in Meru, an almost deserted wilderness, she had found happiness; the hours when Ted was away and at work—and they were many—were not lonely for her, for she was essentially a person who was content with her own company. When later she had children, she shared her attention between them and her husband, giving him always the things he needed and, indeed, demanded, for Ted, kind, tolerant and pleasant though he was, was a very demanding man!

But he was also very devoted and efficient. That afternoon he and Else had taken us down to the pens where the six 'white' rhino from Zululand had been placed not so long before. Their installation had been a personal triumph for Ted, for it had taken him four long years of negotiations to bring them to Meru. They had been moved from the ship at Mombasa in slow stages beginning with one month's quarantine under the

Warden's care in Nyeri where Ted often visited them to keep contact. By the time we saw them they were quite settled and thriving under Ted's conscientious supervision and care. It had taken them only five days to get used to each other and another ten days to become accustomed to their surroundings. Ted planned their days as carefully as the modern mother plans her baby's routine:

Let out into the paddock 7.00 a.m.
Graze until 11.00 a.m.
Rest under a convenient tree until 2.00 p.m.
Wallow and graze once more until 6.00 p.m.
Gently herded back to their pens by a ranger.

Before letting the rhino out of their pens in the morning, their temperatures and pulse rates were recorded and every three days blood slides were taken and examined. Toni and I had previously shown him how to do this, a procedure which some people took months to learn, but which Ted picked up almost at once. He had developed a method whereby he enticed the huge animals to the fence by means of salt water which they loved and which brought their heads within reach. With just one small nick of a razor blade sufficient blood would ooze out to make the slide. The microscope was ready at a nearby table, and we had shown him what it was he had to look for. A wet slide examined almost at once revealed the presence of the trypanosome through its intense movement which soon caught the eye and could later be confirmed in Nairobi by means of stained preparations. It was this parasite which could kill by causing what in man is known as 'Sleeping Sickness', and for which Ted had to be ever on the alert.

The rhinoceros had come from a 'tryp' free area where the tse-tse fly, which transmits the deadly disease, had been eradicated through spraying many years before. We expected the rhino to build up an immunity but this might take some time. The main thing was to tide them over the initial months when they were very vulnerable through lack of immunity and change of environment. As it turned out, all six rhinos had high blood parasite counts, showing a reaction to this by a rise in temperature. Some developed more complicating symptoms, such as swelling, and had to receive immediate treatment. The more vicious of the group could not be hand injected and had to be treated by means of a projectile (dart) syringe.

Ted, with wonderful optimism, was looking forward to the time when his rhino herd would be completely acclimatized and breeding in Meru Game Reserve. The first had already been achieved a year later; the herd was moving farther and farther away from their pens as he widened their pasture, always under the supervision of the rangers who had obviously caught his enthusiasm. Perhaps a passer-by or even a well-informed person might not perceive the enormity or the significance of what he saw: for nowhere in the world had a group of rhinos ever been herded before; not hand-reared, man-accustomed creatures but adults captured in the wild.

The next day, after a reviving swim in the rock-pool, we got under way just after dawn. Ted gave us his driver and promised to come to Mugwongo by lunchtime, by which hour we hoped fervently that the operation would be over and all would be well. Coming to Meru Reserve, unhappy though the occasion was, did much to rid us of the city cobwebs. Everything was so fresh, so vast, so unspoilt that even with the morning's work hanging over our heads we could not help but rejoice every inch of the way. We felt hopeful of the outcome; after all, why should a lion, adult and in good condition, not be able to withstand the rigours of surgery and prolonged anaesthesia? Neither of us had ever removed a lion's eye, but that did not really matter. The actual technique would be no different, we supposed, from that practised on a dog or cat; it was the anaesthetic and careful moment by moment observation of our patient that would be most difficult. It would almost certainly take two of us working together on the operation, which meant that there would be little time to spare for anything else.

It had always been so, in large animal practice; no sister to

78

place each instrument neatly and unasked into your hand, no nurses, no anaesthetist, no post-operative clinic. For years I had worked under such conditions; not with lions, admittedly, but cows and pigs and sheep and horses out in the open, at the mercy of anyone who agreed to assist. Thank Heavens that there were two of us, for this lion was more than just a patient, he was a test case of a new concept in rehabilitation. His adaptation, his behaviour *after* the operation would be all important; it would prove whether or not a one-eyed lion can survive in the wild, a lion that has only begun to be part of the wild.

George was ready, waiting. He had tried very hard to lure Ugas, sleepy though he was, inside the special lion enclosure in the camp, but had not been successful. We would have to operate where Ugas lay, outside the fence. There seemed to be a great number of onlookers that morning, not counting the camp staff. The four 'Bisletti' lion cubs named after the Bislettis, who had given them to him three months before, had arrived in full and irrepressible force and seemed determined to stay. He had accepted the gift with pleasure, for the rehabilitation of a tribe of seven would be even more interesting than that of a tribe of three. He had lured the playful cubs away and persuaded Boy and Girl to keep a respectful distance with the help of a gratis meat meal. We badly needed George's help and would, in fact, be depending upon it. I looked at his face and wondered: would he be able to stand the strain of seeing his own favourite lion undergo the stresses of fairly extensive surgery? Would he be able to give assistance with the anaesthetic just when we needed it most?

We decided to put up a temporary sun-shelter by means of canvas supported over four tall poles. They would protect Ugas's and our heads as the sun became too hot and also offer shade to the medicaments which we would use. Ugas had already received an early morning injection of sedative from George; we now gave another which soon produced light anaesthesia and in addition a tranquillizer which would help the lion to relax. Then we waited for half an hour to see the

79

result which gave us a chance to lay out instruments and cloths in the order that they would be required and cleanse the wound site with surgical soap. He did not object to this so we began to shave the hair from the eyelids above as well as below, by which time we were able to turn and place him into an advantageous lateral position on a clean sheet, swathing the rest of his head with sterile cloths.

We had already prepared the leg veins for intravenous injection, hoping to use as little anaesthetic as possible so as not to produce a too extensive depth of anaesthesia. Just enough and no more is what we were aiming for and we would need George to give small amounts into the vein as it was required. To lessen the reflex sensitivity of the eye structures we also injected local anaesthetic solution at the back of the eyeball, where the main nerve supply to the eye and orbital tissues entered the orbital cavity.

Everything was ready. Toni and I had scrubbed up, the lion was in an ideal state of relaxation. I looked at George just before the scalpel entered the flesh; his face was pale but composed. He answered my look with a nod. It seemed that he knew how much we were depending on him. The eyelids had been sutured together as soon as the local anaesthetic solution had taken effect, its efficiency measured by the simple prick of the scalpel-blade point. Now it was a question of carefully incising the skin each side of the eyelashes, not through to the eye but between the layers of the lids, thus leaving the conjunctiva (lining of the eyelid) to be removed with the eyeball. If left in, this tissue would cause weeping of the cavity.

At this point Ugas's breathing became more laboured and he showed signs of unrest. I left Toni to continue, took the prepared syringe and asked George to help me raise the vein of the back leg. Then I injected, very slowly, one cubic centimeter of anaesthetic solution at a time, until his breathing slowed into an even rhythm and the restlessness ceased. 'Can you carry on now?' I asked George. 'Just hold the syringe firmly next to the leg and *don't* let the needle slip out. I'll tell you when to inject a little more.'

Ted Goss talking to one of the six white rhinos while in
quarantine in Nyeri

Toni and I diagnosed radial paralysis

Four months later Ugas's eye was healing well

Her superb soft coat and feline elegance impressed us deeply

Preech attacked and played with carefree oblivion

I looked up. George's face, still grimly determined, showed signs of stress. As I tried to assess his state I noticed that his forehead was shiny and moist. 'I'll be fine,' he said, answering my look. 'I do feel a bit queer, but it will help having something to do and being able to sit down to do it.'

I left him there, kneeling, his hand beautifully steady as he held the vital syringe in place. 'He's marvellous,' I thought, 'quite tremendous, in fact, no less than we would have expected of him.' Toni had separated the eye from the surrounding muscles. I passed the long, curved forceps to clamp the eye-stalk which contained the retinal vessels which must not be allowed to bleed. Already there was quite a show of blood from superficial arteries and veins, but it was not excessive. The main thing was to imprison the large vessels at the back of the eye. We worked slowly steadily, listening to the breathing, watching the colour of the mucous membranes of the gums. Colour gave a very good indication of anaesthetic toleration, of the general state of the body defences, and of any sign of imminent collapse. But all was well. The muscles of the eye had been cut through, the stalk was now safely ligated and secured. It was time to remove the eye itself and begin to sew up. 'Two cc.s more, please!' I had turned to George, who at once injected the required amount. We needed about ten more minutes of anaesthesia; after that the syringe could come out.

I had always found eye operations rather gruelling, somehow more personal than any other surgery I had ever had to perform. Toni and I both felt the same about it; we were very glad that George could not see too much from where he was now sitting, asking every now and then how we were getting on.

Then it was out. The cause and source of so much pain and aggravation had at last been separated from the body. We would be taking a very close look at the eye itself later on, when it was all over. When we did we found that the iris, that contractile structure which regulates light entering the eye, had been pierced through by a sharp stick and irretrievably injured.

We began to suture the edges of the skin together; when the line of stitches was almost complete, we packed the cavity with antibiotic solution and a powder-saturated bandage, leaving one end protruding from the inner corner of the eye. Over the whole wound edge we sutured a gauze pad as an added protection and painted the surrounding skin surface generously with antiseptic solution. George pulled out the syringe while I massaged the vein in case any of the anaesthetic, a very irritant substance, had escaped. We removed the cloths, washed the blood from the rest of the face and packed up the instruments. I asked George to begin calling Ugas's name; after a few minutes the lion stirred, after an hour he was sitting up, quiet and evidently without pain. George, Toni and I went to the hut and drank tea in silence. I think we were all much too full of gratitude for the smooth course of the morning's work to express any outward thoughts at all. It had taken us two hours from beginning to end, including premedication. By that evening Ugas should be moving about, by the next day he might be showing signs of hunger. The operation had been a success, now the anxiety of aftercare was about to begin. In my experience felines were the very devil to restrain from self-damage; how on earth was George going to prevent Ugas from pawing at his wound?

We left late that afternoon. Ted and Else had both come to fetch us and had been amazed to see the patient sitting up in the enclosure. We had somehow managed to lift him on to an improvised stretcher and placed him next to George's tent, a much safer place than the high grass unenclosed stretch where any wild lion with a grievance could get even with him. As it was, George could now watch him carefully and feed him tranquillizers as he gradually returned to normal. We had given George a sheaf of instructions, day by day notes on the aftercare for the recuperative period. Temperature checks, wound to be watched and kept clean and free of flies, bowel movements kept soft, general restlessness to be controlled with tranquillizer fed in meat. George would have his hands very full, if our half-wild 400-pound feline patient followed in the footsteps of his domestic cousins! 'Whatever happens, don't let the patient escape,' we instructed George, whose features had returned to their normal suntan hue. 'Keep us informed by radio call and we'll be back, unless there is need sooner, in fourteen days to remove the stitches.' George, almost radiant with relief and overflowing with gratitude, saw us off. 'It's not finished yet,' I warned him. 'You may see a great deal more of us than you bargained for. And please try not to let him tear the wound to pieces!'

'Don't worry, I'll look after him,' George promised bravely, 'and if anything happens I'll let you know at once.'

'Let us know anyway, just to put our minds at rest,' I called out of the window as we drove off. He didn't hear me, but I knew that he would do so; he understood that after that morning's work we were almost as deeply involved in the lion's fate as he was.

George was as good as his word. Several messages reached us indirectly, saying that Ugas was well. From the seventh day on we heard no more until a letter arrived from George, written on the fifth day. 'Ugas is beginning to get restless at being shut up,' he wrote, and mentioned that he was increasing the dose of tranquillizer. We didn't say much to each other but I knew Toni's fears were the same as mine. From the sound of George's letter, Ugas would probably not stay in camp much longer, that is, *if* by the time the letter reached us he *was* still in camp at all.

'No use worrying,' Toni said philosophically, 'we'll soon know.'

Yet, by this time Ugas might have pulled out the stitches, his wound might be a maggot-infested hole. He might have escaped, never to return because he had lost faith in the one human being he trusted. He might have been set upon by a pride of vengeful lions who knew that he was too weak to defend himself. So many 'mights' and four days to go until we would know for certain. How could *anyone* be as patient or as fatalistic as Toni, when there was so much at stake?

Our temperaments were very different, I reflected thankfully, as I tried to calm myself, just as our working methods were at opposite ends of the scale. It had always been like that, since the time of our studenthood. I had got into a complete dither just before examinations, while Toni sat, composed, his eyes closed, 'drawing out' what he had put there months before. When I had tried this method, the result had been extraordinarily unrewarding; instead of inspiration, I got only a sleepy feeling and the confirmation that my own knowledge was sadly limited.

It still was, after all these years. 'You have no academic knowledge whatsoever, but your patients recover much more consistently than mine,' Toni often said, when we were on a case. It puzzled him a little, but he accepted it. My practical work, in which I revelled, was more dependent on intuition and finger-tips than the names of the underlying muscle layers as I cut down into them. My storehouse of knowledge contained entirely different information, the sort that he could not retain for a single moment. His own birthday, for instance, and in which drawer his socks were *always* kept. The mundane everyday practicalities of life escaped him altogether and he insisted that the grey matter would suffer a loss of efficiency if working on more than one track at a time. That meant that when he did remember to bring me roses it was so special as to border on the miraculous, especially as he did not pass the flower market on his way back from work.

We enjoyed working together immensely. The operation on Ugas would have been extremely hard for anyone to perform alone and the knowledge that there was so much at stake would not have made it much easier. In spite of our worry over the anaesthetic Toni had kept up an almost continuous commentary as surgery proceeded, giving me a textbook account of the names of each structure as we came upon it. Living with him was exactly like living with a medical encyclopaedia, though this did not in the least imply that he was possessed of the characteristics of a donnish bookworm!

By the time we returned to Meru, in spite of a real effort to be fatalistic and resigned to whatever was to be, I had reached a state of extreme anxiety, when all the powers of relaxation at my command could not restore my equanimity. When we arrived, once again by air, we found that Ugas was there waiting for us, the eye not at all what I had imagined. It looked dry, the line of healing excellent. When, in fact, I removed the stitches with the help of light anaesthetic, each one of the fourteen I had put in were in place, an unheard of occurrence in a cat! However, Ugas's convalescence had had its tribulations after all. As I had suspected, Ugas's restlessness had reached a climax on the seventh day and he had leaped out of camp in response to ominous roaring from a wild lion. From then on he had come and gone from time to time, giving George an occasional chance to administer antibiotic tablets and ointment. The gauze strip bandage had been removed after forty-eight hours according to our instructions. Not even that small wound at the inner angle of the eye had remained open, but the whole suture line had healed quite perfectly. Ugas looked extraordinarily well, his behaviour no different than before. He was, in fact, much more amenable to George since the cause of his pain had been removed. I had certainly learnt a lesson: confinement of ophthalmic postoperative feline patients was definitely the worst course to adopt. They needed occupation, something to take their minds off the irritating, itching healing wound. If free, and unrestricted, they behaved like model patients. What a pity I had not known this years before; but it was never too late, and many others after me might yet benefit from the lesson that Ugas had taught us.

Four months later George sent another report which pleased us immensely. Apart from anything else, Ugas's one-eyedness seemed to have given him an extra ration of sex-appeal, for he was having much more success with the girls than ever before. He wrote:

> The loss of the eye does not appear to inhibit Ugas's activities in the very least. Frequently he goes off for three or four nights at a time. At least twice if not three times, he

has mated with wild lionesses. He seems just as alert as ever. Only difference being that he is constantly turning his head to the right to enable his left eye to take in the lost view on the right side. His judgement of distance does not appear to be impaired.

It would take a great deal of time until anyone could truly say whether or not the operation had been a success from the point of view of his continued rehabilitation into the wild with the new handicap. Eighteen months after we removed his eye he was still doing well, his behaviour as normal as any other lion's. When he disappeared for a week at a time George naturally was very much more anxious, yet his anxiety for the pride, even for the young Bisletti lions who had learnt to kill for themselves, would always be there. He could not help himself, for the pride had become part of his own life; not only Ugas but the other six as well—and any other lions that might join them in the future.

6 *The Littlest Leopard*

'WAIT TILL YOU MEET HER and judge for yourself,' Toni had said, infuriatingly mysterious; and that was exactly what I did have to do since our friends proved equally evasive. I did not think that my questions had been excessive, or even out of place—after all, Joy Adamson was a world-famous figure said to romp with lions in the jungles of Africa! Having been endowed with an average (Toni said above average) share of female curiosity I had wanted to know a little more about her ahead of time. As it was, I would just have to contain my impatience!

Thus prepared by nothing more than enigmatic smiles and a few raised eyebrows, I was not in any way astonished to find, while visiting George one sweltering December day, a woman who did not altogether correspond with the popular image. She seemed at first sight to be brusque, almost unfriendly and very preoccupied; she walked straight from her Land-Rover to the living-hut, ordering tea in impatient staccato tones.

She was holding a little bundle very close to her, which, as I was to learn a few moments later, was the main cause of her worry and unhappiness. It was another animal, a foundling to which she was giving all her attention and care, her involvement so great that she herself suffered agonies when it was not well, but rejoiced equally when it was thriving.

After some moments, during which she seemed to be recovering, she unfolded the little heap and gave a deep sigh —ending in that characteristic half laugh of hers as if to say, 'Well, here we are, now I am ready to talk.' She looked up and smiled and this time her expression was cordial, her eyes crinkling at the corners. The tension had left her, the dust settled; now she looked much more like the Joy Adamson I had imagined.

I walked towards her and saw that she was caressing an adorable leopard cub, her hands gloved in protective gauntlets and that he was only twice the length of her hand. It purred as she stroked the minute, furry body, already lithe and spotted, though obviously thin. She sipped tea with one hand and fondled it with the other, her murmured soft-accented endearments a mixture between English and her own Austrian tongue. I saw that her eyes were full of tears even as she smiled. What an incredible play of emotion within one person! Her deep involvement with her charges, mixed with a very artistic temperament and an almost childish wilfulness made her life like a quivering column of mercury: one minute ready to burst, the next registering below zero.

'I am so sorry I did not greet you properly just now,' she apologized. 'You are Toni's wife, aren't you?' Before I had time to reply she continued, her thoughts bubbling up in short bursts. 'You see, I am so worried about this little one. He had diarrhoea and though he is still taking the bottle I know how dangerous it is for him to be ill. He is so sweet, isn't he?' She had pulled out her already prepared feeding bottle and put it to the leopard's mouth. He responded at once and began to suck greedily, the little drum-like stomach distending as we watched. My veterinary sense rebelled at once, for full-milk formulas were contra-indicated when the digestive system was already disturbed. Joy didn't know I was a vet, but she did know that Toni was one. He had come over at that moment and stood beside me, very tall and handsome, an imposing personality, and I noticed that Joy looked up at him with admiration in her eyes.

'Toni!' she said with emphasis. 'Please help me with this leopard cub. He was given to me by missionaries who had found him deserted. I think he is about five weeks old, judging by his teeth. What shall I do to stop his runny tummy?'

88

'Sue is a vet, too,' Toni said modestly. 'She has been more in touch with this kind of practice than I have. What do you suggest?' he added, turning to me.

'Oh, how wonderful,' Joy exclaimed with genuine pleasure, 'to do the same work together. You must be such a help to each other.'

It was wonderful, Joy was right, though years before I had held quite different views. 'Two vets in one family is one too much,' I used to say to my parents. 'Imagine the conversation! There would never be room for music and art, or even for literature except perhaps the Veterinary Record. At night we'd be doing "post-mortems" on the day's work and during the day we would spend hours trying to decide who was to do what. It would be intolerably dull.' I had stuck to my guns and in the end had married an engineer.

But it was far from dull now, though I could have hardly known that eighteen years ago. I had achieved some interesting moments in life during my eight years of vet practice previous to marrying Toni. I had been asked to treat a leopard, had post-mortemed an elephant, had had monkeys and snakes among my patients. But mostly they had come to me. When Toni and I had at last joined forces, we had discovered that our individual veterinary knowledge covered different fields, and that we complemented each other in a way we never would have done had we married years earlier. We had become 'flying vets' literally, reaching our patients by plane.

I was only here because of Toni, who hated going anywhere without me. The idea of sharing work was very new to both of us; starting so late in life didn't seem to matter in the least. Perhaps just *because* we were older and more mature we were able to divert from our professions and together enjoy so much more than veterinary work: music, travel, the underwater wonders of the sea, literature, philosophy, even Peter Sellers (whom I failed to see as very funny), good plays and many friends. But mainly we enjoyed each other; two years, five years, maybe even ten—whatever it was to be, we accepted it gratefully as a gift from heaven.

89

I would have to be very firm about the leopard cub (it looked so like a kitten!) for it was most important that from that time on and for the next twenty-four hours it drank nothing but glucose-water and salt. After that on to half-strength formula, whatever that had been, continued until things returned to normal. I had with me some life-saving stand-by streptotriad tablets, which, though primarily for human use, worked well on animals. I could never afford to travel anywhere without them, for since I had caught a particularly persistent 'bug' in South America years ago, there was always a danger of recurrence. I divided one tablet into sixteen parts—really just a small particle to be crushed into each feeding bottle for five days and that should do the trick, which it did, though Joy naturally had her doubts.

'What do you think, will he live?' Her flow of questions was irrepressible, her anxiety very real. How could anyone be certain of success, especially with a leopard cub. They were so entirely different from lion cubs, so much less placid, less predictable, less understood! Leopard, as most realized, were very dangerous creatures to raise, even with loving and careful handling. They had a tendency to turn and inflict injury even on those whom they knew well and who cared for them.

If Joy had any failings, lack of courage certainly was not one of them. Her spirit of adventure was enormous—almost too much for one individual—and danger, for her, was a phase of life to be ignored. Being too much aware of it meant living at half-pace, with doubts and uncertainties creeping in to cloud the days. Even when Joy was forced to admit the presence of danger it did not deter her from her mapped-out task, which, at that time, apart from caring for the leopard, was the rehabilitation of her cheetah female, 'Pippa'.

This involved keeping a careful check not only on Pippa, who responded to her call even from a distance, but later on the cubs, who were naturally wilder and often difficult to locate. To watch, to learn about their behaviour meant track-ing miles and miles into the bush each day. Sometimes she would get only a glimpse, other times she found only the footprints. When she did locate them she fed them just enough to keep them linked to her, even remotely, for this was the only way she would not altogether lose them to the wild. Her work was fraught with danger and many of us worried a great deal, not the least her husband George. In a letter she wrote us, describing the cubs, she briefly depicted a scene where she and her scout were pursued by elephant, one of the most frightening experiences imaginable:

Today we ALMOST got into trouble with three elephants who appeared silently while I was preparing the meat for the cubs. I looked up—there was a cow, bull and small calf —the bull coming straight for us within some twenty yards. I dropped everything and ran—and men too—luckily the Game Scout grabbed his rifle and fired during the next minutes four times into the air—but the bull was determined to get us and we had to really run fast before he turned.

'Do come back to camp with me,' Joy suggested over lunch. 'Perhaps Pippa will be there. I would love you to see her.' We were very tempted to stay on, but it depended on Ted. It meant another night and flying back to Nairobi the next day, which was Sunday. Our family would not worry, as we had not exactly specified our return; we had not really known what had to be done. Ted agreed. I would go back to camp with Joy; Ted, Toni and George would stay together for a few more hours, then Ted and Toni would fly back to Leopard Rock before dark. Someone would pick me up after dinner. That would give me quite a few hours with Joy, something I looked forward to immensely.

Her camp was fifteen miles away from George's, but as roads go, it took about one and a half hours to reach it. We had already seen a wealth of wild animals both from the air and on the way to Mugwongo the day before, but at this time, late afternoon, there seemed to be more than ever. The eland were very shy, but in great numbers. Ted had told us that he estimated up to seven hundred in the Reserve; we must have seen a goodly portion of that number just between one camp and the other. We spotted two rhino, mother and calf, but they didn't wait to be admired either. Only two gerenuk stayed where they were, long necks stretching up into thick bush, front legs off the ground, eyes on us as we passed. Game wasn't really used to vehicles yet. Even the elephants had their doubts, flapping their ears as they gave way. Joy pointed out buffalo, lion and cheetah spoor on the road, missing nothing with her sharp, bush-orientated eyes. Walking in this kind of country, thick and lush, with visibility very low, must be quite an experience, day after day. It should have been frightening, but it wasn't, as I discovered quite soon; one was always far too busy watching and listening to think about anything else.

Joy's camp lay quite near Kenmere Lodge, once beautifully appointed, now almost derelict, an unsuccessful effort to create a sumptuous tourist stop, built perhaps five or even ten years too early. She had put up a sign: 'Scientific Experiment' to keep visitors away. She did not believe in encouraging the inquisitive, for to her nothing mattered as much as keeping her cheetah undisturbed. She lived very much alone, and though she loved her life and her location, she quite often felt lonely. She enjoyed people of her own choice, yet abhorred human company if it interfered with her work. I wondered, as we exchanged views and experiences, at her colourful personality and her butterfly mind which moved from subject to subject as she spoke. She could be classed among the almost too highly gifted few, for her versatility was immense. Artist, behaviourist, botanist, writer, photographer; she seemed like a restless genius whose spirit moved too violently, too creatively inside her. She hardly knew to which world she belonged and her dilemma often caused her mental suffering and restlessness. I longed to teach her to relax; perhaps later that evening I would get a chance. From something she had said, I sensed that she had an interest in Yoga culture and philosophy.

She really had made a lovely home for herself among the trees. Below flowed a stream which, during torrential rains, rose to river dimensions, right up to the tents. Everything was neat and spotless, the female touch very much in evidence whichever way one looked. Here there was no protective fence but perhaps there should have been, for many of the large inhabitants of the Reserve looked upon her territory as a through-road. Her bedroom tent was always open; considering the nocturnal visitors of which she told me, especially the felines, it would have been extremely wise to close the flaps. But, as I found months later when I actually slept in a camp-bed next to hers, the night was too lovely to shut away, the early dawn far too beautiful to miss. Her dining-living tent was charmingly appointed, the walls lined with remembrances and photographs of her many ventures, including the *Born Free* film cast, both human and animal. The little leopard was put into its own box-run next to her bed, secure, cared for, asleep most probably until the time of our return.

After a long cool drink we set off with one scout, gun slung across his shoulders. We headed for the little bridge across the stream into the long-grassed shrub, keeping silence except for Joy's voice calling Pippa from time to time in a special melodious sing-song manner she always used for her cheetah. At this time Pippa was thought to be pregnant; her teats (apparently numbering eleven) had been enlarging visibly. Knowing her favourite haunts gave Joy direction for her search. We followed a game path for about half an hour and then stopped. In whispers Joy explained that she would now divert and circle. Perhaps Pippa had given birth and was hiding her young. It was clear that Joy was worried about her because she had not seen her for several days. As we filed along a partridge flew up beside us, startled, but the birdsong and the insect hum continued, for our rustling footfall might have been just another antelope or buffalo for all they cared—or was I misjudging them? Did all the creatures of the wild keep a watchful eye for intruders not of their kind who might disturb their peace?

Scents wafted towards us as the breeze headed them this way and that, some sweet like orchid or honeysuckle, some like wild mint. The way was sprinkled with wild flowers, yellow, red and white heads among the long grass. Once we heard a snort we could only guess at, and a few grunts. Perhaps there were many eyes upon us but we could not see them and perhaps they knew that our intent was innocent, that they need not fear. The sun was getting low; time to return. Joy was disappointed for Pippa had eluded us, but she promised to show me photographs of her when we got back to camp.

'One day,' she said, as I admired the beautiful cheetah in the picture, 'I shall write a book about her and her generations. There is so much we don't yet know about how they bring up their young and everything that happens afterwards. I do hope she is all right,' she added, the old loving anxiety returning. 'I shall go out again first thing tomorrow.' The cheetah, shy cat of the open plains rather than the forest, diurnal, not nocturnal as are most other cats, possessed traits which were specific only for itself. The life and behaviour of the cheetah was a new field of study, especially when the animal studied was not entirely wild, when it allowed the observer to approach and be part of her life. In spite of the friendship, Joy knew that one day Pippa would leave her entirely and that she belonged to no one, but only to herself. She would study her and her cubs as long as she could, and then one day she would go back to a house with modern comforts. But even as she spoke about it she put it out of her mind; leaving her animals was a thought too painful to bear.

The little leopard, still asleep as we sat watching the sunset, was to die less than three weeks from that day. Not of dysentery from which he had recovered very quickly, but of tick fever, for which he was injected in a nearby clinic. Twenty minutes after the injection he was dead, the heart unable to cope with the stress which the too powerful drug had put upon it. 'He gnaws his teeth against everything he can find,' she had written just before, 'preferably my finger.'

Poor Joy! I thought of her, probably alone, with her 'little one,' as she called him, breathing his last in her arms. She must have suffered agonizing grief, for she had given everything of herself, poured her whole being into him. That sort of 'giving' is so intense that bereavement comes as a terrible shock.

It is merciful that most of us cannot foresee what is to come, but are permitted to live each moment as it is given to us. Thus we sat that evening contentedly sharing the farewell glow of the sun in the west radiating dusky-pink towards the glimmering, soft white awakening light of the stars. On the far side of the camp compound I could hear the murmuring voices of the cook and scout, blending into new sounds of the evening; the choruses of frogs, the awakening of the nightjar, the softly hooting owl somewhere in the distance. With less movement, less intensity of light the sound of the African night seemed like the even heartbeat of the earth itself; partly at rest, partly awake, sunset the signal of the changing rhythm.

7 *Pippa Pippa!*

TAKING A BATH under the stars and the rising moon is not only good for the soul and essential for the body but extremely romantic as well. As I lay, half draped in the comforting hot water which Joy had most thoughtfully prepared for me, I could imagine my city sister's horrified face peering at me through the shadows, her voice shocked and distressed: 'And you expect me to come and visit you in Kenya which, you say, is the acme of comfort and civilization, just to be dragged off into the bush to expose myself to lion, elephant and rhinoceros?'

I suppose I was exposed; at least there was certainly no protecting curtain or sheltering wall. If a lion *had* wanted to taste my soapy skin he could have done so just as any straying rhinoceros could have pitched me, canvas bath and all, high up into the air. But who, once bewitched by the African night, ever gave a thought to *such* hazards? Oh, if I could only transmit to her even a fraction of the magic of the murmuring bush, that feeling that all the world belongs to one and that one belongs to the whole world!

Joy Adamson, whom I had seen often since that first meeting, was sitting in discreet seclusion behind the tent wall; not only had she provided me with a steaming bath but was keeping me company as well. 'How few,' I wondered, as we exchanged thoughts and memories, 'would ever believe that *this* is reality and that the smoky drawing-rooms, the cocktail small talk, the social intercourse of the sophisticates is only an illusion from which we cannot, as yet, separate ourselves?'

96

Rolf's long tongue enveloped the cheetah cub

Preech and his 'pajama' dog

Dorothy Udall and Dawson Marami, the director, and author (from right to left) discussing another *Animal Ark* programme

'You're not nervous?' Joy suddenly interrupted our flow o conversation, for there seemed to be lion grunting somewhere behind me.

'No, I'm fine,' I said obliviously, the utter relaxation after the tired, hot day acting like codeine.

I had flown up from Nairobi only that afternoon to discuss the new children's wildlife television series with the Adamsons. Both would play an essential part in it, or so it was hoped.

I breathed deeply, feeling wonderfully invigorated, the city stresses once more thankfully left behind. 'Are you practising relaxation?' Joy must have picked up my thoughts, for that was exactly what I did seem to be doing. From the depths of my moonlit tub we discussed wildlife, Hatha Yoga, diet, sex and our varied experiences while adapting ourselves to past and present husbands—comparing notes, so to speak.

Eventually, regretfully, I rose and dried myself and prepared for bed.

'Bless you,' I thanked her, as I entered the living-room tent, feeling utterly refreshed; 'that was the nicest bath I have taken in my whole life.'

I had dined alone with George that evening and had been driven to Joy's camp by his temporary assistant, Hans, who almost undid the effect of the delightful three hours I had spent at Mugwongo by switching off the lights every time he saw an owl, hare or nightjar on the road which he negotiated at breakneck speed. After making several quite unheeded pleas to my altruistic driver who insisted he was only respecting my philosophy of non-violence, I became more and more certain that our humanity would, indeed, be the very last thing we would ever be aware of.

After that the moonlit bath had been sheer heaven and the early night that followed it more than welcome. We had to find the cheetah family the next day and that would mean an early start, for whatever happened, Joy wanted me to look at one of the cubs, called Mbili, who had lost a great deal of weight. Since she had not seen the entire family for almost two weeks, finding them would be a most difficult task.

We had already examined stool samples from all four cheetah; Pippa, the mother and her three cubs, Mbili, Tatu and Whity. Joy used to send them in little dressed-up boxes with any 'victim' she could find. We hardly ever saw the carriers, but just found them with loving inscriptions on our dining-room table on the average of once every two weeks. 'Dear Sue,' Joy used to write, 'here is another present from Mbili, thank you so much for analyzing the last one.' Most creatures in the wild, as well as in domesticated conditions, suffer from some sort of parasite infestation; her little pride, though very well rehabilitated, were still linked to her through food and, where Pippa was concerned, through genuine affection. Joy trekked for hours each day to locate them and was just as anxious as George when she found no trace. Lions often persecuted and killed cheetah cubs, and she had already lost—perhaps to lion—the first entire litter. The dilemma was difficult to solve, for without wishing to keep the foursome tied to her apron strings, she did want to offer them every advantage for a good start. That implied extra vitamins, anti-parasite medication and meat, mainly to 'keep in touch.' Mbili, if debilitated, might well lag behind the pride and fall victim to lions or hyena. She was very active, yet thin, though described by Joy as having the greatest pluck of the three.

We set out towards the swamp, one of the places Joy had not explored the previous day. 'That's the place where Ted Goss had his accident.' She pointed to an open patch next to the track, beyond the point where the Land-Rover could be taken. I saw a large stony clearing in front of us, long yellow grass and acacia woodland on each side.

'Poor Ted,' I thought, remembering all the details, the nightmare he had suffered here in this very spot, where a year before he had been trampled by a near-immobilized elephant. It had been agreed upon that he would not attempt to immobilize for marking purposes without George Adamson to protect him, yet on that day he had taken only his scouts, for George had been too far away and it would have taken too long to bring him back. Toni, George and Ted had immobilized giraffe and buffalo together not so long before, for, like Barrie Chappell, Ted ardently wanted to learn the new methods of scientific conservation. When the elephant attacked, he had fallen into a hole in his urgency to escape, and the scouts had not acted quite fast enough. When they did finally shoot and kill, unable to use the minutes when Ted was under the huge body, he had been severely injured, escaping death in some wonderful and miraculous way. With Else's help and nursing he had recovered fully, but even so it had taken a year of pain and patience.

'Pippa, Pippa, upsi, upsi, tralalalala,' Joy sang enticingly across the wilderness, her vivacious staccato melody more like something one would expect to find in the Austrian Alps than in the African bush. She continued, happily, hopefully, then stopped and began to study the tracks on the ground. 'Another cheetah has been here, I can see only one set of spoor,' she explained. When I looked closely I could clearly define the four toes, each toe preceded by an indentation, the nail-mark of the unsheathable claws. 'Look,' she said, walking slowly with head down, 'this is a warthog, a split hoof, but very small. Lots of them; they usually move about in families.' Quite near and in contrast were the tracks of a rhinoceros, huge, the pad print merged with the three toes in front. 'I think Pippa will have gone this way,' she said suddenly as her own scout pointed to a fresh set of cheetah tracks at the side of the path. 'That's where she found her mate last time, we must go and look.'

We returned to the Land-Rover and she asked me to stay, for to approach the whole pride with a stranger might be difficult. She promised that she would bring them back to me, and that I would get a good view. 'That big bull elephant is a bit nasty sometimes,' she said, pointing towards an enormous specimen peacefully feeding at the side of the road along which we had just come. 'If he comes too close don't stay in the Land-Rover in case he turns it over. And don't try to drive back either, because he is blocking your road and the way forward ends in a swamp. The left side is very rocky and rough and would break the springs and the way I am going is hopeless too. Just shin up one of these trees,' she said sweetly, 'that's about all I can suggest.' With that she disappeared and I went on an exploratory walk to see which of the tall, slim trees I would pick if I had to. Having done so I returned to the Land-Rover, opened all the doors to create a good breeze and began to read the manuscript of Joy's cheetah book, which she was in the process of writing.

Every now and then I glanced at the elephant who was now facing me, but he probably could not have cared less about my presence. 'I wonder if elephants have ghosts,' I thought rather morbidly. 'If they do, I might see Ted's assailant appear at any moment.' But if he had any thoughts of coming he must have had to postpone them, for at that moment Joy appeared, hot, out of breath and ecstatically happy, for she had found her foursome—yes, *all four*—and was about to bring them to the tree-stump a few yards from where I was sitting. 'Thirteen days in the bush,' she poured out her good tidings in spurts and starts; 'they *can* manage alone, isn't it wonderful?' Before I could agree, she had collected her tin of milk, her jar of calcium powder and her basket of meat. Almost at a trot she and Twithenguru set off again down the dense slope to fetch the gang, her feet hardly touching the ground.

To have found them at all, I thought, was a marvellous feat in itself, but to bring them back, following voluntarily as they were, was quite fantastic. For the next hour I watched them, entranced, quite near enough to see almost everything they were doing in detail. Pippa and her three cubs, appearing one by one, played, drank from Joy's milk tin and ate the meat she offered. Alert, protective, Pippa, in radiant health, guarded her fourteen-month-old litter while they frolicked about. She allowed herself to be fondled and caressed but not so her young. As soon as Joy took too great a liberty they flashed away from her, just out of range. The meal finished, they relaxed, replete, while Joy took photographs. She pointed to Mbili and spoke her name, very relieved that she was after all in good shape. There was, in fact, very little difference between the well-grown trio—at least to my well-trained eye. Joy looked completely at home among her tribe. All signs of strain gone from her face, she looked ecstatically happy.

With vivid mime, she told me about the cubs' new teeth, and the ticks that she pulled, or tried to pull out of their fur. She had her bottle ready to make a stool collection, very methodical, forgetting nothing. After a while the foursome began to play, leaping up into the branches where Joy had suspended some meat on the end of a long pole. I had seen them when they were younger, and more dependent on their mother. Now, to all intents and purposes, they were ready to be launched into a life of their own. A month later Whity had killed a duiker, final proof that she could fend for herself. Suddenly Joy blew me a kiss and pointed to her, a sign of gratitude for what we had done. I wished that Toni had been with me, watching our patient playing in the morning sun. Watching, I remembered what had happened to her only six months before, a very short time for a leg, exposed to the extreme stresses of everyday cheetah life, to recover so completely.

Joy had radioed us to come immediately and asked us to bring everything which we might need to repair a leg injury. We had been able to go almost at once, making use of a guest who was only too willing to take over the care of the children and household. What a relief just to make a list of what had to be done, cancelled, bought, fetched and put to rights and to place it in capable hands. When we had landed at Meru everyone had been waiting and ready for us, and we went at once to Joy's camp, only a mile or two from the place where she had seen the cheetah family that morning. George was there too to give assistance and moral support, though she asked if he and I, non-essential to the first part of the operation, would remain somewhere between camp and the cheetah. She would approach alone first of all, to feed it the doctored meat, and then, when it became subdued, send for Toni.

'Please keep absolutely quiet,' she asked us, finger to lips, 'if you make the slightest noise it will spoil everything.' After that admonition she left with her faithful scout, gun slung over his shoulder, disappearing into the scrub almost at once. Her extreme anxiety was not without foundation. While Toni and I had been away in India during the Christmas vacation, Dume, one of the four, had been injured and flown to Nairobi where he had died, not of his injury, but of a feline enteritis which he had contracted in the city. Since that time, and because of the disruption in their lives, Pippa and her remaining three had become much more wary and difficult to approach.

The askari did not return until two and a half hours later, which we had spent in quiet philosophical discussion in the shade of a wide-spreading tree. Waiting in the middle of the wild is never a hardship; we were entertained by the ringdove, the wood hoopos, and the many talkative shrikes who must have wondered what three people were doing for such an interminably long time under their thorny acacia tree. Toni took the carrier bag, which was to carry the fifty-pound cub, and strode off into the boiling midday sun while George and I settled down to wait, he to puff at his pipe and I to plague him with questions, to write and to relax.

Toni, it later transpired, had been led about half a mile through thick shrub to where Joy had found the cheetah family. Whity had taken the meat, had become sleepy and had remained behind while the rest of the family had fortunately disappeared. Joy, in a great state of agitation, met him about thirty yards from where the cub lay, and in mimed whispers related what had happened since she had taken the drug. She insisted that they approach very slowly, crawling through the bush, and remain hidden in a good vantage point from where Whity could easily be seen.

The cub was dozing peacefully, head nodding, but obviously not unconscious to the world. If Toni thought that his principal trials were the heat of the day or the distance he had come, he now found that he was very much mistaken. Joy, in a frenzy of worry lest the cub suddenly recover and disappear into the thick tangle of thorns, kept up a stream of whispered interrogation and prognostication. 'She won't go to sleep, she will run into the thorns and die,' she predicted tearfully. 'What do you think? Will she go to sleep and when will she go to sleep, and when will it be safe to approach her?'

Toni, no doubt with the same maddening, unshakeable calm that he had so often displayed to me in times of stress, would give no consolation except to say: 'We shall see!'

After about forty minutes the nodding head of the cub came to rest on the ground, which is exactly what Toni had been waiting for. He decided to wait another ten minutes to make quite certain that Whity was truly incapacitated, which gave poor Joy another period of suspense and agony. 'It's going to die,' she now intoned fearfully. 'Can you promise me it will recover?'

Toni, his reaction that of a wary veterinarian who would not commit himself however small the chance of being wrong, answered quite truthfully if rather heartlessly that he could not guarantee anything, which produced further lamentations.

When the time of waiting had expired, Toni and Joy crept towards the cub and found to their delight that she was completely oblivious to the world. Placing her lovingly into the bag, they brought her to our tree and we set off, all five of us, towards camp.

As soon as Whity became restless we increased the sedative for we needed relaxed limbs and body for a thorough examination. Between gulps of cold fruit juice, for we were all completely dehydrated, we managed to pinpoint the exact injury, not a fracture or partial fracture as we had feared, but radial paralysis, the paralysis of the nerve which controls the forward movement of the lower part of the leg, Whity, lying very quiet on the table under the huge 'umbrella' acacia tree, was a most beautiful young cheetah. Her superb, soft coat and feline elegance, so much more marked in a creature who lives wild rather than captive, impressed us deeply as we worked on her. Even as a limp, immobile form she was proud and beautiful, her limbs and body supple and athletic.

'If only cheetah would not be so confident of their tree-climbing ability,' Toni said, 'their bones are just not built to stand shock and strain like those of other cats.' While we prepared a bandage Joy and George stood by, Joy a little calmer, but still distraught, George anxious for the cub, willing to help in any way he could. We wanted to support the leg with a plaster bandage, for that and an injection of concentrated vitamin B was all that could be done at this point: rest, for six weeks, disuse of the injured limb, confinement which would only be possible under the influence of tranquillizers. We gave the first dose by injection with tablets to follow which were to be given in meat at regular intervals.

Whity was now showing clear signs of recovery from sedation, raising her wobbly head to take a look at us. Transported with relief, Joy beamed through her tears, for now it did look as if all would be well.

We left soon afterwards, and received very regular and most methodical reports of our patient's progress and of the tranquillizer dosage she was receiving. Whity, contrary to our expectations, did not take to her imprisonment; whenever the sedation lightened she began to struggle, which could mean damage to the injured—and other limbs. The tranquillizer had to be increased and regulated very carefully, Joy devoting practically all her time to it. Gradually the limp disappeared and a plan for Whity's return to her family had to be made.

Joy, pleased and thankful, now began to worry day and night over the new problem. Would Whity find her own family, would they ever take her back, would she, after all these weeks, show her resentment at being confined and just disappear without a trace?

Joy had written to us, begging us to help her find a way:

The *miracle* solution would be of course if I could induce Pippa to come to camp and collect Whity in perhaps two weeks' time. But Pippa will never bring the other cubs near camp and so this is out of the question. She has within the last $6\frac{1}{2}$ months only been twice *alone* in camp, last time three months ago.

It's terribly cruel to deprive Whity of her WILD life and if you *please* can think of a way to get her to her family—please let me know as soon as possible.

I had replied that I was sure that if anyone could find the answer it would be she, for no one could understand her cheetah pride so well.

I shall never forget the day I received her jubilant and very beautiful letter in which she described, in a way that only a loving mother can describe her young, the final outcome, undreamt of by us all:

I felt most unhappy about the whole situation. It seemed such cruel irony to have to *tame* Whity for several months until I *might* lead her back on a leash to Pippa—as after the first failure of enticing Pip into camp there seemed no alternative. In the evening I could *not* get Whity into her sleeping quarters—so had to leave her in the large compound. She sat on the roof of the small hut and for the first time allowed me to feed and caress her while in a position to bolt from me. During the night two lions roared close—I felt most worried. The last three days searching for Pippa had been exhausting and she might have by now crossed over the Rojoweru near the bridge. When returning to camp at lunchtime today—I collapsed and was sick from the heat—how could we carry on this double job—looking after Whity to get her friendly when half the day I had to search for Pippa? As I did not know now *where* to search—I sent Guitu early morning to the Tamarind to look for Pip—While I attended to Whity's feeding, cleaning compound, etc.—and if no sign of Pip at Tamarind, decided to drive to Rojoweru bridge and search the area there again. I still felt very dizzy from the heat.

Suddenly I heard Guitu calling: Pippa, Pippa—and before I knew more—she came rushing across the rivulet over her fallen tree bridge leading straight to Whity's compound. Whity rushed most excitedly along the wire—

prr, prr, prr, while Pip looked puzzled—they licked each other through the wire—then Pippa sniffed at the straw behind the compound where I always discarded Whity's droppings—while Whity got frantic to join Pippa. Meanwhile the other two cubs appeared just across the rivulet —calling Whity and she replied. Quickly I opened the compound door—but Whity passed it several times without realizing her way to freedom was open. I had to manoeuvre her carefully in position to see the opening and—*out she was* near Pippa. Both went on the tree-bridge and stood there for some time. I was terrified that Pip would go ahead without Whity following and then both would be separated by the rivulet. But Whity kept glued to Pippa who returned to my tent. Meanwhile the other two cubs had crossed the rivulet near the kitchen bridge and I had all the family in camp. Whity seemed overjoyed to be with her sisters, all were *so happy*. If people think that animals have no facial expressions of emotions—if *ever* there was a happy cheetah cub—it was Whity now. She had had such hard-frightened eyes all the time in camp—now her eyes were so soft and laughing and radiant again.

To me it seemed like a miracle; small, perhaps, compared to the many daily wonders, yet enormous on its implication, for the climax of this drama was as natural and harmonious as many everyday dramas that abound in Nature, though almost all of these remain invisible to our unseeing eyes.

8 *Yoginis at Large*

HILDA STEVENSON-HAMILTON, friend of my pre-Kenya days, had the kind of eyes that saw deep into Nature. Almost seventy, she lived alone, remaining in her lakeside home after the death of her renowned husband, Colonel Stevenson-Hamilton, pioneer of the Kruger National Park.

The homestead, a series of little cottages strung together, was situated high up above a lake, smooth lawns sloping down to the water's edge. I often stayed with her. As the evenings drew to a close we would sit on the open veranda and watch the night begin. The sunset lasted longer and the air was cooler but then we were not hugging the Equator as we did at Meru. Since I had left, little changed in our friendship; we kept in touch by letter, and I stayed with her whenever I went down to see my family.

I often thought of Hilda when I was with Joy. They were worlds apart, yet had much in common. Both akin to animals, each working closely with a different type. Joy first with lions, now with cheetah, Hilda with lions too and now with zebra. Both were good artists. Hilda painted animals, Joy flowers; both had the gift of true portrayal, of absolute sincerity in their expression of art. When Hilda put brush to paper she created something so alive that it was almost startling. The leopard had dragged his kill into the limb of a tree, or into a cleft of a rock to protect it from the ever-present scavengers; the irrepressible wildebeest were playing, nervous, agile, vivacious. Under her hand the sable antelope looked noble, the eland regal. Joy's flowers always seemed to shine in the sunlight, transmitting colour, texture and scent from the page of a book. Though of different origin they both contained the same effervescence, in letter as in speech. They loved faraway, remote places, disliked the pressure of social obligations and were both so thoroughly outspoken that many took it amiss.

I missed Hilda keenly; in moments of nostalgia my thoughts returned to her and the tall gum trees beside the house, and the call of the oriole as he flitted against the windows trying to see his own reflection. Hilda possessed the most wonderful quality in the world: humility. Her dearest wish was to remain anonymous and to live in the shadow of her husband's image. I was sent a copy of an article she had written for a magazine, *Fair Lady*, a summary of her philosophy, a reflection of her love for animals—touched by her inimitable humour:

Robert Louis Stevenson-Hamilton in family prayers asked: 'Give us courage, and gaiety and the quiet mind.' My New Year resolution, I think, is to endeavour to live up to these things. And afterwards, when this life is over, if given the choice, I would like to come back as a Hippopotamus in the Kruger National Park. To paddle past the house at Skukuza, on the Sabi River, where my husband and I spent so many happy years. To clamber out of the water at night and ponderously walk along the hippo-tunnels to the most succulent grazing. To be able to inflict a formidable bite, but not to have to take life to exist, as do the beasts of prey. To dream in the sun on a sand-bank of whatever hippos dream of and to take to the water when it gets too hot. To know the bottom of the river like the back of one's foot. To stand, almost awash, with other smiling hippos propped in sleep, amidst wonderful surroundings, is to know contentment which is the secret of happiness. Yes, I resolve one day to become a hippo in the Sabi and will never, no never, have to worry about my figure!

Hilda used to laugh about *my* Hatha Yoga figure-reducing efforts. When I first met her I was struggling hard to bring down my weight and my waistline and, among other things, to learn self-control in the matter of eating. 'Just today,' I would say, excusing myself to myself as I put more cream on my porridge. We had many discussions on the subject of Yoga, for both the physical and spiritual aspects of it were beginning to interest me deeply. One year after meeting Hilda, I became a vegetarian and, though she had always been tolerant of all my foibles, this rigid new routine seemed just too much for her to endure. She was certain that I was undergoing acute suffering and tried hard to induce me back into the realm of the *omnivors*. With a nicely browned, dripping hot sausage held up over my plate she tested my strength, which she insisted was superhuman! I tried to explain that I was more earthbound than most, but that giving up meat was no sacrifice at all.

I had done meat inspection, I had seen, felt and smelt the horror of an abattoir. I had witnessed the terror of creatures who sensed something was going to happen to them, even if they didn't quite know what. I had also seen the lack of hygiene, knew the illnesses that resulted from eating unclean meat. Finally, I had come to know the one thing which so many seemed to doubt: that one's daily protein can be derived from foods other than meat, fish or eggs, which I had also relinquished. Man doesn't need meat to survive; it is only a luxury item on his menu. What I found hard to understand was how people who loved animals and worked with them could eat meat when other foods would do just as well.

Hilda, who was like a second mother, friend, confessor and teacher to me, was really worried, for a time anyway. 'Soon you'll be giving up milk, cream and cheese,' she predicted. 'How will I feed you then?'

'Good heavens,' I answered in mock surprise, 'I am not an eccentric. I'm only a vegetarian at present, though I can't exactly predict what the future has in store!'

Slowly Hilda, who ate far less meat than I had in my pre-vegetarian days, came to realize that I would survive, and that my increased energy and improved health must, in some way, be connected with my eating habits. About the time I left

White River I had a feeling that she might slowly change, though she had never admitted it. Well, here it was, in black and white, and even if her determination might not be realized in this life but the next, it nevertheless showed the trend of her thought:

> to be able to inflict a formidable bite, but not to have to take life to exist. . . .

Hilda, ever tolerant, her mind always delightfully open to new thoughts and practices, nevertheless found my involvement with the world of Hatha Yoga a little bewildering—though intriguing too. During my weekends with her I could do more ardently those things which I normally found difficult to fit into my everyday life. Practising Hatha Yoga was one of these, especially in the early mornings before breakfast. Hilda came to know that when she entered my room she might expect to find just about anything. I might be on my head, or my shoulders, breathing in jerky rhythm, rocking on my stomach, tied into an irreversible knot (or so she thought). As she entered I would continue, and when I looked up I would find her sitting on my bed, smiling her enigmatic smile, looking as one does at the acrobatics of a chimpanzee in the zoo. She used to say that she enjoyed the entertainment, feeling that this phase would pass. As long as I didn't try to persuade her to rock on her stomach she didn't mind what I did.

For me, Hatha Yoga meant a new lease of life, for at the time when I found both it and my new diet I had been at my lowest ebb, mentally as well as spiritually. The longer I abstained from meat, the less I wanted it. Gradually my mental outlook changed until I could hardly believe that it had ever been different. I studied eastern philosophy and found the answers to many of my questions, questions which had haunted me from early childhood. Terrifying death, the end of everything, I now discovered was only a transition. Like everything else one had to search, to train, to study to 'tune in' to the higher worlds where no knowledge was ever withheld to the sincere seeker. I found that the eastern philosophy I followed quarrelled with no religion, but accepted all teachings, all men as equal. When I went to church I enjoyed it far more, for now I knew that there really was a way 'up' and that I would find it myself one day.

Hatha Yoga was part of all this, though primarily to us in the West it must be taught as a physical culture. It was the antidote to tension and all that this implied. Healthy body, healthy mind—the harmony and balance between both. I had never intended to teach but somehow, before I knew it, the necessity to do so had just come upon me. First I practised alone, then with friends who noticed that something wonderful was happening to me. After six months we were ten on the carpet of a friend's house and I suddenly realized that I must *learn to teach*! After all, it was not only a matter of knowing the breathing techniques and the postures. It was a matter of watching very carefully those who needed special help: the asthmatics, the arthritic sufferers, the slipped disc and ulcer patients, the people with dislocated hips. I blessed my medical background but decided to seek the advice of my own teacher who lived and taught five hours' drive away from my home.

Sam Busa, master teacher of Hatha Yoga, one-time champion wrestler, body builder, weightlifter, masseur and physical culturist lived and taught in Johannesburg. I went to as many classes as time allowed, but could not let it interfere too much with my veterinary practice. 'You can either teach or you can't,' he said. 'You can learn basic Hatha Yoga from me and you can watch me and other teachers teach. You can read books. But the gift of teaching you cannot learn. It is a gift from above. You'll know soon enough if you have been endowed with it.'

To my surprise teaching did seem to come to me very easily. I loved it and all the responsibility that went with it. More formal classes started and I found a friend, a nurse, who also loved to teach and could take my place when necessary. By the time I left the Lowveld Hatha Yoga had become very popular and spread as new pupils began to teach. When I came to Kenya, there was the same demand.

Gradually the classes increased in number. People came from all walks of life, men as well as women. Overworked secretaries whose bosses needed to learn far more than they did. They came to regain their endangered health and cure the chronic ache of their backs. Above all, they came to learn the art of self-discipline and self-control so that they could better tolerate the man behind the big desk! Overweight ladies came to have a last try at reducing, underweight ladies to put on weight. They had heard that the cell structure found its own balance by the constant practise of complete breathing.

Many came because the doctors had given them up: permanent injuries, chronic pain, migraine headaches, constant muscle cramps. Each one was a different case and needed something special; yet all who came and who felt the beginning of peace and relaxation found new faith and the knowledge that there is practically nothing that cannot be healed, provided they wanted to be healed. Peace of mind, concentration, deep, full, rhythmic breathing, loss of tension, return of tone, of harmony and of suppleness. At the end of three hours of teaching, when I should have felt tired, I felt renewed and exhilarated. The energy force which had flowed into my pupils through their efforts had reached me too, in some mysterious way which I could never explain on a mere scientific level. Perhaps the vibrations of twenty or more men and women, their minds simultaneously fixed on peace and harmony, were so strong that they enveloped everyone. As they entered the hall I asked them to shed their worries in the doorway and in doing so forced myself to do the same.

Men came for a host of reasons and needed very special handling. So many things enter into the pupil-teacher relationship when one teaches a physical culture, the least of which is not sex. When I placed my hand on a handsome pilot's stomach to feel whether or not he was really beginning his breathing movement correctly, I tried hard to make myself sexless. I thought I had already managed to learn this difficult art in veterinary practice as a special gesture to farmers who found it hard to consult a female veterinarian about the breeding problems of their cows and bulls. But there at least, I was working from a distance. When the pilot's respiration increased beyond normal I realized that I had not successfully

achieved my object and retreated, trying to convey my message from a more discreet distance.

Although Hatha Yoga must be done seriously and regularly if anything is to be achieved with it, it is by no means a dead-pan practice. I have never counted less than five good hearty laughs during one hour of teaching, apart from my own private ones which I always tried to stifle. Men, who came because their wives had bullied them into coming, or who really only wanted to ogle at the black-tighted figures, were the most amusing. They had much time to spare during postures and were horrified to be caught out peeping at their neighbours.

'Anyone who turns their head even one inch towards their neighbour while standing on their shoulders is in danger of an immediate dislocation of the neck!'

This injunction was often followed by a tremendous bang as some horrified male lost his balance while he too quickly tried to turn back his head. The muscle man, the champion hockey and squash player came to class, certain that Hatha Yoga was only for the ill and the weak. But he came, nevertheless, to convince himself that he could achieve it. When he found that he could not even bring his head halfway towards his knees, either standing or sitting, he became distraught, amazed and determined. Since suppleness of the spine is one of the secrets of eternal youth they worked very hard, for vanity must be included among the hosts of reasons why people have embarked upon a daily ten-minute Hatha Yoga routine.

Toni, who had been a Yoga addict in our student days, also joined the advanced class, making his entrance almost always ten minutes late. This, I suspected, was in order to miss one of the most strenuous but most beautiful of all postures, the 'Salute to the Sun,' with which I usually began. Not only was he late, but he was the most rebellious of my pupils, doing the very thing which causes more heartache to a teacher than anything else: he didn't listen. When I remonstrated with him he insisted that this was his revenge for all the days I wouldn't listen to him!

With a benign, happy smile on his face, such as he wore when (as he admitted) he was enjoying the murmur of my contralto voice as pleasant background to his thoughts, he simply worked in his own rhythm and to his own time, his mind far away, beyond the class, probably dreaming of a bigger and better radio-telemetric device. When we performed the bow-posture, which, being lean, he found most difficult, he suggested that Yoginis (female Yogis) had the unfair advantage of being able to balance on several specially designed and very resilient areas of tissue with which men were not endowed. One thing he shone at: relaxation. At the end of the class, when everyone had reluctantly got up out of their blankets, he was still horizontal and quite immobile, a beatific expression on his face.

Joy, too, had wanted me to try and teach her to relax. I explained how it might help her, for she freely admitted she was in need of something which would give her tranquillity and stillness of mind. She lay on the floor of her tent and I showed her the deep-breathing technique. When she had mastered that, I attempted to quieten and halt her over-active mind, yet even then her thoughts came tumbling out. 'Don't talk, just relax, relax, relax. . . .' It wasn't going to be easy, for she was possessed of a mercurial explosiveness that would need a daily discipline of practice which she might not be prepared to give, not yet, anyway.

Somehow my work with animals and Hatha Yoga had always been linked. Man can learn so much from animals, if only he took the trouble! The best spinal exercise I knew was called 'Cat Stretch' for very good reason. To me the sight of a cat, rising and stretching out of sleep, is symbolic of relaxation, of unconscious release of tension not only from the spine but also from the whole body. The grace and ease of movement of a creature that is free of mental tension is beautiful beyond description. Perhaps in the end, living close to animals might bring a permanent cure of all our ills—that and a little help besides for those who need it.

9 *Hyrax in my 'Choo'**

LIVING IN CLOSE PROXIMITY to animals—wild or domestic—does not always, however, have an enriching effect. At times, and often due to the human influence, the animal may deteriorate and/or adopt some of the characteristics of the owner. In veterinary practice this transfer is well known; it may be one of neurosis from man (more often woman) to animal or it may be an uncanny ability on the part of the 'pet' to imitate the owner, or even pick up some of his habits.

Many factors seem to play a part in the success or failure of a healthy man-animal relationship. One of these is the size of the animal relative to its environment and the adequacy of its living quarters. The most endearing monkey, when confined in too small a space, might turn destructive out of sheer frustration. Here temperament, inherent or 'inherited' through human contact, must be taken into account. If the handler is consistently calm, firm and kind, the animal knows what to expect. If temperamental, it will get edgy, apprehensive, even fierce. I have never once heard George Adamson change his tone of voice when controlling the lions, his own behaviour pattern being far more predictable than that of his pride. When Ugas refused to get down from the Land-Rover roof, I wanted to pull his descending tail and make the urging much more forceful. Not so with George. He coaxed him down inch by inch, showing no sign of anger, impatience, or even wear and tear!

---

* Swahili for 'loo'—pronounced U rhyme with 'oh'.

In a veterinary household, such as ours, animals and humans come and go in profusion. The former can be classified according to their status: home-owned and permanent, patients whose length of stay is indefinite, object for study often transient, and last, but by no means least, animals travelling with their owners. We owned two dogs which, Toni said, was ample, since our already overcrowded home was so near a main road. One of these was an aged Alsatian male with immense loyalty, intelligence and forbearance who was also possessed with a most useful quality (unusual in a male dog), a strong maternal protective instinct. The second canine was a medium-sized, 'anybody's guess' crossbreed, who, in spite of her emotional vocalizations and great attractiveness to fleas, endeared herself to all in our menage except animal visitors. Devoting herself wholly to the business of eating, playing and exercising, she lacked completely any motherly trends, rather despising the infant orphans and others who stumbled towards her with hopeful expectancy.

The number of rooms we had in which to accommodate our friends had always been altogether inadequate, thus enhancing the discomforts of our guests enormously. Nevertheless, by the time we had hung some beautiful paintings on the flaking walls and Toni had built some enormous shelves for our magnificent collection of earthenware pottery and rows of books, by the time the mats, rugs and curtains had been placed in colourful array, the house really did acquire a special and quaint homeliness. When we were overflowing with visitors, it looked more like a camp than a residence, with stretchers and sleeping bags tripping one up at every turn. We didn't mind, if they didn't mind. Mostly our friends were used to a haphazard existence, for they were involved in some form or other of wildlife work. Those whose tastes were more formal and sophisticated loved it as an unusual experience to tell their friends about. So many delightful unique personalities had crossed our threshold that we felt we had come to the end of all surprise—until a certain day when the hyrax moved in.

For the record, a hyrax is a rock- and tree-haunting

mammal, whose special claim to fame is its relationship to the modern elephant, by virtue of its digestive system and hoof-like feet. In appearance it is a small, plump guinea-pig-like animal about the size of a large rabbit. The hyrax in question was a tree-hyrax, grey, brown, longish fur, no tail. He was equipped with more than adequate tusk-like teeth which he used most efficiently and with lightning speed. Some say that, considering his small size, he is the most ferocious animal in Africa!

It was on a Sunday and they had warned us: 'Expect two plus four.' The little garden cottage was ready and made up for them, and dinner had been organized for nine. Some friends were sharing Sunday late tea with us on the lawn when the Savidges arrived: John, warden of Ruaha Game Park in Tanzania and his attractive physiotherapist wife, Yvonne. Gail, in an inspired moment of domesticity, had baked the most enticing chocolate cake, but the Savidges would not even sit down. Their entourage needed to be fed, exercised and housed, so we left them to it: one large tree-hyrax weighing seven pounds, one sparrow-hawk, hooded and in training and two baby tiger-tortoises, far less demanding than the other two. Just then our bearded, bachelor, naturalist author friend, Colin Fletcher, arrived with an empty void in his stomach, and place for chocolate cake. He had become ill on safari and this was his first real meal; he swore it cured him, the heap of cream and chocolate and the lively company that evening!

It was an oversight on my part not to have prepared for Pimbi, for the hyrax had to be fed within the hour, but we did not really know where to find the sort of food it relished. Just as I was beginning to feel guilty at the hungry expression on Pimbi's face, I remembered Jean Brown, our red-haired, sylph-like ethnologist-librarian friend with a weakness for tribal dress, Hatha Yoga and hyrax. 'She'll know where to find the food Pimbi loves,' I assured Yvonne. 'Let's go and get her.' In the end it was Colin who organized the expedition and picked up Jean, ever willing to lend a helping hand, be it to human or hyrax.

The children and dogs had lured the tea-guests for a walk in the nearby arboretum, and I went indoors to make up the spare room for our other guests, Hans and Ute Klingel, arriving from the northern wilderness of Maralal, where they were studying Grevy zebra.

'You're going to have a full house tonight,' Toni commented. 'Shall I go and buy some more food?' Even on a Sunday evening this was possible and sometimes very necessary, for unexpected guests usually managed to find their way to our house just about that time. Our life-saver was a store aptly named the 'hole in the wall', where practically anything could be bought at a time when, by law, all other shops were closed.

Fortunately that evening I did not have to avail myself of Toni's kind offer, especially as I knew how allergic he was to pressing the starter button of the car on a peaceful Sunday. He sat down on a chair and thoughtfully watched me change the pillowcases. Something in his manner suddenly caught my attention; perhaps it was his too angelic face, or the way he leapt to his feet to pick up something I had just dropped.

'Darling,' I said, sitting down on the bed, 'have you got something on your mind?'

'Me? Why?' Toni smiled in a way that meant that he knew that I knew.

'Come on, let's have it, what do you want me to do?'

Toni rose to his feet, gave me a bear hug and said, 'Do you know, I think you're wonderful. You can make beds, you can make love and goodness knows what else! I wrote to Tony Mence and told him that you can also lecture on animal post-mortem techniques.'

'You what?' I couldn't believe it. We were due to fly to Tanzania the following week, Toni to lecture to the students of the African Wildlife Management College, I to keep him company and maybe fill in the odd gap in basic veterinary teaching such as I had given previously: diagnosis of disease, first aid, simple veterinary techniques. But not post-mortem! I didn't have time between now and Friday to work up the material, even if I had had it at my fingertips. 'How could you! You told me it was going to be a holiday.'

That was all I had time to say, for at that moment we heard a Land-Rover pull up in our drive, which meant that the Klingels had arrived. The bed was not made, supper had not been started, the tea-things not even cleared away. Thank heavens it was Hans and Ute, who were so easy-going and such marvellous company.

Just at this moment the hyrax foragers appeared with the children and tea-guests not far in their wake. The Savidges came from their cottage in search of liver for the sparrow-hawk, but of course, as vegetarians, we hadn't even a crumb of steak. Suddenly, after half an hour of absolute peace, the house became like Nairobi Airport on a Sunday afternoon. I immediately gave the children lots of errands while Toni went off to get some beer for our guests. Ute and I finished the bed (they were easy guests who didn't mind sharing one between two) and caught up on the past months; Colin Fletcher and Hans sat down to talk about zebra, the tea-guests took their eave and Yvonne, having gratefully received the hyrax's supper, retreated once more down the garden slope. When she returned she brought Pimbi with her, saying that he really wasn't safe in the presence of the sparrow-hawk, who, though hooded, might like a morsel of hyrax instead of liver. Besides, Pimbi might well be lonely.

She decided that the lounge was the safest, cosiest place and proceeded to close all the windows tight shut. While John, patient and silent, held him, she investigated the rest of the room.

The chimney needed blocking, the fragile knick-knacks moving, the flowers the Klingels had just brought had to be moved in case they got eaten. My large plant which dominated one corner of the room was too big to be moved and had to take its chance. Books, papers and records had to be put out of harm's way. Finally Pimbi was installed and the dogs banished. The children thought it was all wonderful, had their supper early and went off to bed. The guests, eating an informal meal on their laps, soon found the lounge very stuffy indeed and gathered round the dining-room table. Jean Brown arrived and joined the lounge group to admire the hyrax which had firmly installed itself under the settee. Toni and I, with warnings to be quick about opening and closing the lounge door, went from one group to another, trying hard to be hospitable to both. The Klingels badly wanted to hear the new wildlife record, but Hans had got into a huff with the hyrax, and the Savidges would not consent to having the door even an inch ajar. In the end the party broke up before eleven, which was just as well since the division of the household was getting a little too much, even for me. Everyone was tired, the hawk had been for a walk with John to get used to the city atmosphere, and after half an hour of cajoling and threatening in turn the hyrax was extricated from under the sofa.

We left them and said good night. I noticed that they disappeared into the bathroom with the hyrax but was far too tired to wonder why. My last thought in bed, after another discussion on the merits of teaching the future game wardens of East Africa post-mortem techniques, was for the lodgers of our cottage. 'How can all six of them manage in that small cottage?' I asked Toni. 'Shouldn't we give them another room?'

'There isn't one,' Toni murmured as he put out the light, 'so don't suggest it.'

The next morning everyone seemed to stir unusually early. As I organized the household and the children, I kept running into one or other of the Savidges with either hyrax or hawk. I set the breakfast table, made sure Toni was doing his morning Yoga exercises and took the children off to school. When I returned I found our faithful Maria, the laundry lady, standing dumbly in front of the children's door with a bundle of ironed clothes. As I approached she pointed to something that seemed to indicate that entrance was forbidden. I looked up, and there, upon the door, a notice had been pinned which read like this:

which meant: Danger! Hyrax inside. You are not to go in—
and be careful to close the door!

Surely, I thought, Pimbi could not have joined the snake
and chameleons and Jessie, our black dog who always hid
under Gail's bed in the mornings. To 'dehyrax' the children's
double-partitioned room would take days, for their walls and
shelves and desks were decorated with anything from sheath
knives and spears to Chinese pottery figurines. But Pimbi *was*
there, perched on Guy's curtain rail as if he had never lived
anywhere else. The windows had been sealed tight shut, all
fragile articles hidden in drawers, photographs stacked with
the books. No wonder I had heard the children stir so early,
they must have arranged it all the night before!

It might have gone well from then on, had it not been for
the fact that Hans and Ute Klingel slept in the room which
was separated from the children's by an adjoining passage.
Every time Yvonne went to see if Pimbi had settled in and had
enough to eat, the door was slammed after opening to go in
and slammed after opening to go out. Then the same thing
was repeated on the way out with the door leading from the
passage to the hallway. The zebra behaviourists were very
tired after their long, rough journey; being shaken almost out
of their beds on the average of four times every twenty minutes
did not amuse them. They got out of bed and devised a new
notice—in English: 'Please close the door *very* quietly!' Then
they went back to bed. I was sorry for them but couldn't
suggest a remedy. By the time Toni emerged, everyone had
left the house to go about their errands. I left shortly after, but
not before telling the servants to be sure to keep the children's
door tightly shut. I need not have bothered; they were far too
frightened of the hyrax to take even one step into their room.

That night things went more smoothly. Gail and Guy were deliriously happy to have the hyrax happily installed in their domain, even if I did banish him to the lounge for one hour so that I could air their room before they slept in it. The Savidges were happy because Pimbi was more settled and the Klingels were happy because doors were being treated like cotton wool. As sometimes happens on 'blue Monday', Denise Morchand, our glamorous American friend, dropped in to see us, complete with a new sky-high bouffant hair style. She looked so lovely that she took everyone's mind off the hyrax and entertained us vastly with her rather half-finished tales about white (professional) hunters. She knew a great number of these, having once been their publicity liaison officer. Being thoroughly eligible, she had been hunted high and low since she had arrived in Kenya.

As an avid and aspiring journalist, endowed with immense enthusiasm, she usually managed to persuade one or other of our wild (life) guests into an interview on his work, taking copious notes in longhand. When there were no visitors, Toni always obliged her, for she could never get enough information on the controversial subject of either elephant cropping or immobilization of wild animals. More French than American, she seemed far too fragile to bear the brunts of Kenya life. When she didn't come on Mondays nor contact us for several weeks, I would get extremely anxious, for somehow we felt responsible for this bird-like Dresden china girl who seemed quite unable to cope with Kenya men. But in the end she always did turn up, bearing a gift offering in her hands as if to make up for the worry she must have known she was causing us.

'Have you finished with the bathroom?' Ute asked after Denise had left and we were all retiring to our different ends of the house.

'Won't be long,' Yvonne sang back cheerfully, 'depends on Pimbi.'

At this point my curiosity overcame me. I left the tea-trolley standing where it was and made a dive in the direction of the guest bathroom section. I managed to get to the 'choo' door just as Yvonne was disappearing and persuaded her to let me in. 'Just exactly what do you do with him in there?' I asked. 'Surely the lavatory isn't a very good imitation of where he usually "does it"!'

'Come in and see,' Yvonne said invitingly, with a look of a doting mother on her face. 'He is so regular that I can always depend on him doing it in the proper place. Just sometimes when we travel he gets disturbed and then his timing goes wrong. Do you know,' she added, 'he'd rather get constipated than "do it" anywhere else. Sometimes he will do the goods over the washbasin, seems that any such hole does the trick.' Toni, who had put his head in to see what on earth was going on, just happened to catch the end of the sentence. I saw his face twitch nervously as he withdrew, murmuring good night. His stomach never was very good over a matter of droppings in the washbasin; he could cope much better with cow dung in the right place. I was sorry he left in such a hurry, for as he fled he caused quite a commotion, stepping on the black dog with the super-endowed vocal chords and jingling the Greek bells which hung in the entrance passage.

'Shhhhhh,' Yvonne protested, finger to her lips. 'If you disturb him he might not *do it*. He is so sensitive to strange places and sudden sounds.' We returned to the 'little room', but not before I had banished all canines, locked the front door in case of late visitors, stilled the copper bells, asked the Klingels to be especially sympathetic and patient, and closed the lavatory windows to keep out all sounds of traffic.

'Now!' Yvonne had placed Pimbi, no doubt 'in extremis' by this time, into the lavatory bowl itself, his lower end suspended over the water's edge, his upper body clinging tenaciously on to the edge of the bowl. We waited breathlessly but not for long, for at once he extended his arms and lowered his body farther until his rump almost touched the water. He then excelled himself by an almost immediate delivery of a stream of hard, small pellets, followed by an adequate supply of liquid. When he had finished, Yvonne lifted him out, and

124

complimented him on his achievement. 'You're very honoured,' she said, hugging him to herself, 'he sometimes won't perform in front of strangers.'

I flushed the lavatory and followed Yvonne into the slumbering children's room, where Pimbi immediately reinstated himself on high, this time on Gail's side of the curtain rail. 'Can she watch tomorrow?' I asked and pointed at the slumbering form. Yvonne thought this over for a moment, then smiled and nodded and said good night to Pimbi, while I went to kiss the children in turn and tuck them in again. Gail, fast asleep, smiled and threw her arms around me, mumbling something which sounded like hyrax.

We crept out of the room and parted ways, Yvonne to find her way down the slope to her cottage, her husband, hawk and tortoises, I to bring the glad tidings of success to Toni, who was impatiently awaiting me. 'It's fantastic,' I said at the end of my detailed description, 'fantastic, that such a creature, even if it does have a wonderful animal like an elephant for a relation, can adopt such human habits; better still, to be able to limit the natural functions of the body to one outpour a day. Did you know that your friends were such gifted animal trainers?'

'No,' Toni replied somewhat flatly, 'I didn't. I knew "the noble savage", as we used to call him, in the days before he married. Strange,' he added as an afterthought, 'he used to be a lot more lively. Doesn't say much now, wonder if I'll end up like that . . .'

'Never fear,' I assured him, 'you haven't the adaptability that John has. In spite of your insistence that you are the quietest man you have ever met, I still think that in any normal after-dinner conversation, we average out about ten to one; the ten being your average. Don't you think that Pimbi's habits would interest a behaviourist? We must tell Hans about it when he returns, see what he says.'

We had first heard of Hans when we visited Zululand some years before. The Natal Parks had once again asked Toni to come down to help them solve yet another immobilization problem; how to deal with the nyala, a beautiful antelope sparsely distributed throughout Africa, whose temperament was very different from that of the kudu or the waterbuck, for instance. Like any animal that is nervous, its response to drug darting might well be quite unpredictable—which it was. Shortly after our arrival, while being taken around the Umfulosi Park to assess nyala locations, the Land-Rover engine went on strike, some hours walk from anywhere. 'Where's the nearest habitation?' I asked, ready to strike out into the 'bush'.

Nick Steele, the warden, told me that the nearest camp was that of a young American who was studying wildebeest. 'He stays out there alone for months at a time, living on a handful of raisins and nuts,' he said, 'and he studies the wildebeest standing on his head. Seems to make them less apprehensive.'

'How very interesting,' I thought, 'he must be a fellow Yogi.' If the rangers, tinkering with the engine, were to fail in their task, we would have to fetch help and thus meet him. On the other hand, we had passed tea-time without tea and it was not too far from dinner-hour. It would take two hours to reach the wildebeest addict, and there might be little for us to eat except nuts and raisins when we got there. Having reasoned it out I decided to change my tactics and stopped willing the repair efforts to fail. As soon as I did, the Land-Rover engine sprang to life—by coincidence, of course—but nevertheless very satisfying in view of the fact that I was weak with hunger.

Years later, and recommended by our friend, Ian Player, Chief Conservator of Zululand, Hans had arrived, or rather burst in upon our household and stayed on. He fell in love with Kenya and enrolled as a first-year student in Biology at the University of Nairobi. He was a very unusual young man, and at first sight seemed to me an excellent example of a behaviourist so intensely influenced by his subject of study as to grow remarkably similar. Having literally lived alone with the wildebeest herd for months at a time, having studied their language and social pattern, he had become unmistakably wildebeestian in every way. When speaking, his flow of words, coming upon one at incredible speed and with huge volume of sound, was often interspersed with just those snorts I remembered hearing when among a herd of the lively gnus: 'Pbfhrrr.' His restless, explosive nature had a disastrous effect upon anyone who might require peace and quiet such as Toni usually did, especially when he came home for five o'clock tea. When, some weeks later, I decided to take the 'bull by the horns' and discuss the problem with Hans he most surprisingly welcomed my advice, a feature for which I much admired him, for few men over the age of thirty will listen humbly to a member of the opposite sex. He promised to keep the late afternoon a little quieter, assuring me that, above all, he wanted to do nothing that should upset Toni.

The following day, coming home from work, a startling scene met my eyes as I entered the lounge: Toni, sitting in his usual place, was reading a book and drinking tea. Hans, having placed himself exactly opposite him, was certainly keeping his side of the bargain; he wasn't saying a word. However, instead of taking up some reading matter, he was sitting in fixed, cross-legged immobility, staring across the room at Toni with folded arms. I realized at once that Toni was far more discomfited by Hans' hero-worshipping silence than he had been by his loquaciousness; his face being that of a man about to explode with suppressed irritation. Quietly I beckoned to Hans and lured him to the kitchen, hard put to know what to suggest next.

'Perhaps we should have tea together in the garden,' I proposed, 'and leave Toni to unwind from his hard day's work alone. Scientists are so terribly sensitive,' I added apologetically, 'and hate being looked at. By the time the rains come and we can't use the garden I am sure he will have settled down.'

Thus it transpired that I spent my five o'clock tea break between Hans and Toni, making sure that both had what they needed, various though their requirements were.

I came to look upon Hans, who was red-haired, tall and athletic, as one of my own children. He was charming, thoughtful and very helpful, begging me to point out any inadequacies which he might well have developed after all the years alone in the bush.

The thing I found most difficult to speak about were his eating habits. In spite of a strong veterinary 'stomach' I found that his morning repast was more than even I could bear. Not content with the normal-size breakfast bowl, he preferred one of the pottery casseroles which I normally used as a 'dish for four'. This he filled with a mixture of wheat germ, yeast powder, sunflower oil, boiled peanuts, raisins, brown sugar and milk, in that order. The result, aesthetically speaking, was appalling, especially at an hour when one's sensibilities are particularly delicate. None of us could understand his python-like tendency or his own ability to digest this marathon hotch-potch of substances. Toni, the weakest digestion wise, turned green for a few mornings, then had his breakfast served to him on a trolley on the veranda. The children began to eat their breakfast in the kitchen, and I gave up eating breakfast altogether.

Yvonne Savidge and Pimbi the hyrax

The Manyara lions are renowned for their tree-climbing habits

Portia looked the most warlike

Hans insisted that he had eaten this sort of thing for a long time, so I felt less entitled to interfere. Apart from certain things, caused mainly by his great enthusiasm and a sprinkling of insensibility, he was an easy man about the house, with vegetarian tastes similar to ours. Could one really advise a grown man on his eating habits? My dilemma, as usually happens, solved itself. Hans had been seeing a doctor, I knew, but I didn't know for what reason. One day, while we sat, undisturbed, drinking coffee together on the lawn, he confided to me that the reason for seeking medical advice was that a strange lassitude was overcoming him during the first three morning lectures. This fatigue was so severe that he often dropped off to sleep, thus missing some vital information and lecture notes.

Poor Hans, he was most distressed and had begun to take some medicaments in the form of pills to keep himself awake.

Now was my chance, but I had to be gentle and tactful. 'Don't you think,' I began, 'that maybe the quantity of breakfast and the mixture you eat are in some way connected with your malady? You see, the early morning stomach is sluggish and needs special care, not a huge and sudden invasion of the sort of food you force it to accept. There is nothing but good in each individual item you eat,' I added, seeing his look of consternation, 'but when these are piled upon each other in quantity, the sum total may result in turmoil of your digestive system. Your blood then pours into the mesenteric vessels, ready to give first aid with digestion, the result being that your brain is drained just at a time when you obviously have need of it. How about reducing the size of your bowl to start with?'

Hans considered my advice for a day or so, then changed his breakfast habits. This made our breakfast hour a much happier one, though Toni stuck to his new routine; I discovered afterwards that he couldn't stand the smell of concentrated yeast, a great pity since a little of it might have gone a long way towards strengthening his own nervous system and

129

thus staving off the strain of having an amateur wildebeest behaviourist living with us.

Hans had been working with George Adamson during his college vacation; a marvellous chance to develop his interest in the African lion. Perhaps for this reason the tales of the idiosyncrasies of a mere tree-hyrax did not impress him, though our next animal inhabitant, this time a patient, completely captivated both him and all of us. 'Preech', as he came to be called by virtue of his typical bird-like cry, was a three-week-old cheetah cub which had been found deserted on the Athi Plains in the company of two litter mates. All three of them were in pathetic condition; bone-thin, dry mangy skin, sparse brittle hair, spine gauntly exposed, eyes matted. Two died within two days, but the third, a male, survived, though stunted, infested with hookworm, pot-bellied, hardly resembling a cheetah except for the markings. We treated him for parasites, which had been severe enough to cause intense anaemia, gave him tonics by mouth and injection, and antibiotics for a lung infection. Why or how he survived we will never know, except that he was obviously meant to live. We mothered him, gave him frequent regular bottle feeds, a place of his own to seek sanctuary in by day, and a warm bed (Gail's) by night. We knew that if he was to live at all he would need something more than just proper veterinary treatment and a balanced diet. He needed, like any orphan, a great deal of mother love, and in our household got this in a rather curious way.

Rolf, our Alsatian, adopted the little cub almost at once. To Jessie's chagrin, he now devoted his entire attention to the rearing and 'fathering' of the little creature. Every time his long tongue enveloped the cheetah he covered him with moisture from top to toe, to which Preech seemed to respond with a burst of new life. When he became stronger, they would play together for hours. Rolf, though such an old gentleman, tolerated the cheetah's special form of tail-torture not only with patience but with obvious delight. The house and garden were Preech's range, though we had to watch him carefully in case he slid out toward the traffic side. After a short time Rolf promoted himself from father and playmate to guardian also, his watchful eye always on the outlook for one step in the wrong direction. We watched with amazement and wonder when he picked up Preech in his huge jaws, head in, and simply removed him from the front-drive steps which faced the main road. Preech made no objection at all, but allowed this procedure to be repeated time and again. Jessie, keeping a wary eye, never once joined in the fun and games. Whenever Preech tried to entice her to make a threesome she growled rudely and retreated. It did seem as if the smell and feel of Rolf's tongue had some sort of healing qualities, for, contrary to everyone's expectations, the cub thrived and began to develop into a very forceful personality, with a 'never-say-die' slant to him!

Gail adored the little cheetah. I thought of my early teens and how I would have loved such a companion. As my own family had not been very 'animal-minded', my pets had been limited either to birds, fish or cats and any temporary stray canines I picked up in the streets of London. Not having had those things which I had then longed for, I continued to 'grow up' and enjoy them through all the years of the children's youth, grateful that my dream had come true, even if not in my own childhood. Gail devised a wonderful substitute for 'mother-presence' which, in the first days, when Preech's life was hanging by a thread, proved the difference between life and death. She put her large alarm clock, ticking loudly, into her 'pajama dog', a 24-inch long yellow remnant of her earlier years, still complete with smooth hair, endearing face and, above all, a functional zip-fastener!

As soon as Preech heard the magic sound of the clock he settled down at once upon the dog's back, stretched in utter contentment over the rhythm of what must have served as a surrogate, an imitation mother heartbeat. She then put the whole bundle between her own blankets for warmth, an environment which seemed to have adequately satisfied all his baby instincts. In this way, with the yellow ticking dog by night and a live dog by day, plus several human nurse-companions, he eventually reached the stage when, at three months, we had to admit to the owner farmer friend who had brought him in the first place, that he could now go home.

Our household was strangely quiet without him. In contrast, the Hopcraft family, numbering anything from nine humans to twelve animals normally contained within their generous farmhouse home, were very conscious of Preech's return. He simply took over, with their consent, the entire cat-dog-meercat circus, even attempting to play with the antelope and gazelle, not included in the initial family count given above, and who lived in an enclosure near the house. Whether dachshund or larger, whether gentle or fierce, cat, dog or otherwise, Preech attacked and played with carefree oblivion, quite unaware of the dangers which could accompany such behaviour. His greatest pal was a black kitten of small proportions which seemed to bear the bites, pulls and scratches inflicted upon him with martyr-like enjoyment. Occasionally he would suddenly extricate himself and gallop off, ears down, fur standing straight up, howling as if his last moment had come. Yet, five minutes later, they had somehow joined forces again and always in the same pecking order: Preech well on top, the kitten entwined somewhere underneath.

He grew well and fast, beginning to consume a whole rabbit or fowl a day, but still maintaining his need for a bottle morning and night. One Sunday when, luckily, we were at home and not out on safari, one of the shyer members of the Hopcraft household appeared, bringing tidings of Preech. Appearing as he did with empty hands, I assumed he had come to tell us of one of the cheetah's latest adventures and invited him to join us on the lawn for tea. 'What has happened,' I asked him, 'is Preech all right?'

He put down his second cup and said, 'No,' he wasn't all right. In fact, he was very worried about him, and so was everyone at 'Kenplains', which was the name of the farm.

'But what has happened to him?' I insisted, trying to make

the young assistant spill the beans; it was like drawing blood out of a stone!

'He has had a fit, we don't think he'll make it,' he replied, 'but we can't think what has caused it.'

I was now beside myself with worry. 'But for heavens sake,' I tried not to sound too severe, 'why didn't you bring him?'

'I did,' came the quiet reply, 'he is in the car.' I took off, as if possessed, followed by Toni and the children and the two dogs who no doubt thought that it was time for a walk. The young assistant had already got up and surprisingly, considering his slow verbal reactions, reached the car door before us.

On the seat lay a bundle in a cardboard box, wrapped in a cloth. We lifted out the whole box and brought it on to the veranda, while Toni went to get the medical bag. Poor Preech! He was hardly recognizable. Although his illness had apparently only begun the night before, he had collapsed completely. He was having a convulsion as we lifted him out on to the table, his whole mouth and jaws covered in froth. His temperature, very high, fell to below normal between bouts of spasms. Then it all started again, the twisted expression on the beautiful face, the contortions of the body. When he did seem conscious, we were almost certain that he could not see.

Whatever was happening, an anaesthetic had to be given at once to still the overstimulated nervous system. Death from nervous exhaustion might well result if we didn't, yet death from anaesthesia could follow as well. There was no doubt at all as to what had to be done, even at a risk to life. As soon as the intravenous injection had been given the little body became calm, the respiration more regular. It was vital not to let him get cold and a hot-water bottle was filled and put underneath. Toni had gone to fetch injectible gluco-saline solution as an antidote to shock and dehydration, while I tried to 'worm' some sort of a history out of the shaken young man. The only thing he could suggest was that illness had begun after a guinea fowl had been given to Preech; and that the bird had been killed with lead shot.

133

Lead shot! The symptoms could easily have been those of lead poisoning. As no other facts would be extricated from him we decided to administer the antidote to lead, magnesium sulphate solution, first by enema, with repeated sedation as soon as the cheetah began to recover from the light anaesthesia. This, with feeding by injection, might keep life going until the time the poison had been excreted. We didn't know for certain that it was really the cause, but in view of the lack of any other possible reason we had to treat accordingly. 'Two lives used up,' Toni said as the assistant left. 'I wonder if he has another seven left to him.'

Second time lucky. Preech had done it again and there was great rejoicing in the house. It had taken almost three weeks to get him really well and of course Rolf and Gail and the pajama dog had taken part in the therapy. Once more, having got even more fond of him than the first time, we had to take our leave of him and return him home. Rolf sadly moped around the house, sniffing the places where they had played together; the bathroom was scrubbed after the day-cheetah box was removed. Soap and talcum took the place of wildcat aroma, rugs and carpets lay still and flat instead of being in perpetual crease and crumple. Even Jessie looked sad, or were we imagining it? Since Preech was now a much bigger proposition as a playmate she seemed to mind his presence less and had even joined in some of the less violent games. 'Chumbi', a little Colobus monkey we were looking after, had got very attached to the cheetah, and, contrary to natural instinct, had plagued him mercilessly whenever she could. From the safety of a chair she plucked at Preech's tail, and if there was no reaction she leapt down in pursuit. Suddenly the chase would reverse, but the monkey always got the better of it, since she could, in one leap, escape to a high platform of safety. I thought that when Preech left, Rolf and she would play together, but I was wrong. The essential link was missing, and without him life just wasn't fun—not for a few days, anyway. The most forlorn of all was the pajama dog, once more tossed aside, the clock back on the shelf. I took him to the cleaners to console him—and the children—and when he emerged from the process he looked better and younger than ever, ready for the next cheetah rescue operation.

Preech was barely eight months old. He was acting more and more like a cheetah, increasing his speed spurts by the day. Although he seemed not to be endowed with any superior intelligence, he felt protective towards his home and his many masters and mistresses, and was beginning to act as self-appointed guard-cheetah to his domain. His teeth and claws had become large enough to be classed as weapons, his body shape and carriage lithe and proud. He often charged in play but soon retreated when reprimanded, for on the whole his courage and fierceness, already in evidence even in the first weeks of his life, were still in the experimental stage. One day, as always on a Sunday, an ox-drawn cart pulled up beside the homestead. Preech charged and got mixed up with the wheels, with the result that by the time he was retrieved, he seemed much the worse for wear and was having difficulty in breathing.

Jack Hopcraft himself came on this occasion and he made no bones about what he had come for. 'I'm ashamed to disturb you yet again but you've got to help us,' he said, anxiety and apology written equally over his finely sculptured features. 'This time I think he has really had it,' he added, 'there must be internal injuries.' We examined Preech for over an hour but apart from a suspicion of extensive chest bruising and possible injury and rupture of the diaphragm, there seemed to be nothing more. Once again he was left with us. He was so large now that the yellow-haired pajama dog was like a toy compared to him. He was too big to get into bed with Gail, almost too fierce for Rolf to play with. This time we felt he belonged less to us, for his existence on the farm where he had unrestrained freedom of movement was what he knew as home. Nevertheless, after a few days, old memories seemed to stir within him and once more he settled down and stole our hearts.

David, Jack's son, who was engaged on a project studying gazelle and other antelope as possible ranching animals, had brought us a Grant's gazelle with a hopelessly crushed leg which I had just amputated. We did not think it wise to leave the gazelle in too close company with the cheetah for it couldn't have known that the latter only wanted to be friendly. Once more, and no less sadly than before, we took the now fully recovered Preech back to 'Kenplains Farm', hoping against hope that from then on he would behave with more discretion.

10 *The Rhino with the Rubber Horn*

THE GAZELLE HAD RECOVERED from the first shock of the operation yet she didn't look as if she were making an effort to live.

She lay in her grass-floored enclosure, head bent sideways, neck stretched back along the body, the typical posture of resignation. When we approached, she responded by lifting her head and permitting herself to be fed by a long-spouted cup which allowed the liquid food to seep slowly into her mouth through the molar teeth. Lucerne and other delicacies were ignored and if we placed them in her mouth she would give a desultory chew, then let everything drop out again, grinding her teeth a little in protest. As soon as we left the run she again took up her former position of utter hopelessness, eyes closed, ears down, her interest in life no more than a flicker. Animals and indeed primitive people can die of nothing more than despair. Once the mind becomes numb the body follows suit, even if there is no actual medical cause for decline. Psychologically, shock and change of environment play a very important part. Take away familiar sounds, smells and sights which create an atmosphere of security and the result is confusion and collapse. The 'tomorrow things will improve' therapy cannot be communicated and, even if it could, would not be acceptable.

'Put her out of her misery,' some suggested, 'what sort of life would she have on three legs, even if she did recover?' How often I had heard this defeatist attitude expressed in the past years! 'Kill,' they said. 'Make it quick, with pistol, by poison or injection.' So easy to snuff out life, so impossible to restore. Painless destruction to order, but *never* in the owner's presence, thus saving the bother of conscience pricks and the nuisance of burial! Wild, semi-wild or domestic, it mattered very little; after all, they were only 'animals', creatures over which man has dominion!

And yet, as if to restore our faith, and bring us a reminder that mankind is endowed with a spark of the Divine, there are the voices of those who stand firmly against needless destruction, such as the owner of the Grant's gazelle. This animal was semi-wild and could return to the paddocks beyond their home; she would be fed and watered, safe from predators, her three-leggedness not much of a handicap. Animals of any species, unless very large and heavy, soon re-establish their balance and move about with amazing agility.

Her life, in the light of a whole species, was of no importance at all, yet it was as important as any individual animal's on earth. She would be cared for and studied; from her medical history, her behaviour, her growth-rate something might emerge which could lead to new knowledge. Now all we needed was an inspiration, something outside the normal bounds of experience, for without it we were in danger of defeat.

The way to find an answer is to stop thinking. It is thoughts, with their long tunnels and mazes that take us away from the simplest truths. 'Stop thinking and listen,' a very dear friend had once said to me. 'It is only when you still your mind that the answers will come; they are there more often than you know but your mind is too full to pay attention.' Years ago Lesley Busa, wife of my Hatha Yoga teacher, who with sure knowledge and absolute faith had given me the answer I needed, hadn't been speaking of sick gazelles. Her philosophy, which later became mine, gave me the key to many problems, both animal and human. It taught me that every creature has a soul and that, if we shirk this reality, our own soul will become tainted by each needlessly taken life.

The children had been just as worried about the gazelle as I was. They worked out a plan which was simple and direct, but one which had not occurred to us; they brought their never-endingly hungry rabbits up from their pen and put them with the patient. They mixed the rabbit food into the lucerne, climbed out and waited. The rabbits began life in their new environment by investigating the recumbent form. They sniffed, touched and jostled it before they set about continuing their meal, making a terrible commotion as they tried to sort out the different kinds of food, just what was needed!

Watching the scene was Andy White, film-script writer from Hollywood who had been sent to us by Ivan Tors to gather ideas for a new film, *Cowboy in Africa*. We had only just met the night before and I still could not overcome my surprise at finding an American film-script writer so normal, so soft spoken, so humble. Having expected a loud, overbearing, gaudily dressed, smooth-spoken 'film type' who had come to ask for advice, but certainly wasn't interested in taking it, I was swept off my feet by Andy's sincere, genuine personality and his immense interest in everything around him. He sat watching the rabbit-gazelle scene with wrapt attention; when the gazelle suddenly lifted its head as if to say, 'Hey, what's going on around here?' I noticed he was just as moved as I was. We sat spellbound and watched the ecological miracle evolve. The gazelle, having taken stock of the situation, now became very mobile indeed, its territorial instincts coming into full play. It stretched its neck forward, and began at first to nibble and finally to eat with gusto, as if to make up for lost time. As it ate, it seemed to gather strength until, warmed by the sun and its own efforts, it rose to its uneven height, sending the surprised rabbits scurrying away from their fodder.

'That's truly marvellous,' Andy said, 'and a stroke of pure genius. If I can weave that into my story I will.' When the first copy of the script was sent to us we were touched and honoured to see that the gazelle-rabbit scene had been included. A new aspect of animal behaviour had emerged. Creatures of the wild, interacting not only with their own but also with other species belonging to their natural environment, are stimulated into a renewal of normal behaviour pattern, whenever natural or near-natural stimuli are introduced. In the end the gazelle did die, quite suddenly and without obvious reasons. The autopsy revealed good healing and no complications. Had it not been adult it might well have recovered, as did the gazelle in the film. Perhaps we should have used a companion of its own species as we did in the case of the injured cheetah later on. An adult animal will not adopt a new way of life as well as a young one; just as happens with people. The rabbits had initially stirred it into life, yet in the end the primary shock and feeling of displacement had been too great.

The film, *Cowboy in Africa*, later named *Africa—Texas Style*, was an Ivan Tors brainchild, inspired by the theme of ranching wild animals in Africa. The concept of preserving wild animals by using them for ranching was not a new one by any means, yet very few people have ever been able to put the idea into practice. Ivan's script writer developed this theme into a combination of the popular American cowboy image and the English farmer in Africa, whose kindliness and foresight and love for the wild finally won him success. Andy threw in a heroic nurse who, though already engaged, falls in love with the cowboy; a lean, harassed scientist who revels in his tissue studies, an unlikely, irredeemable villain, a witchdoctor and a Red Indian assistant cowboy, as well as a host of stand-ins and some imported 'quarter' horses which had to have stand-ins too.

The majority—and by far the most tractable portion of the cast—consisted of a host of animals from buffalo to zebra to gazelle. They had been caught and 'cast' and were being trained ahead of time. In the end only one piece of the jigsaw was missing: the African boy who was to play 'Samson', and who was to provide the central theme of the 'progressive and free Africa'. Andrew (Bundy) Marton, the producer, an extrovert Hungarian with a heart of gold and an artistic temperament, appealed to us to help. Time was running out and the schedule gave him only another three weeks before 'D' day.

I was just then finishing my television series, *Animal Ark*, for which I had gathered a team of children to help me. I invited Bundy to come and watch one of these, at the same time asking one of the cast, whom I thought might be suitable, to come along. It worked. Charles Malinda possessed just those very characteristics Bundy had been searching for: an excellent command of English, an upstanding, sparkling sense of mischief, an unselfconsciousness that was both charming and fresh and a captivating face with a pair of sparkling eyes. Charles's parents were very concerned over the future of their son; they didn't want him to miss too much school, nor become too 'Americanized'. Finally, after they had received a promise that their boy would not be spoilt or kept from school too long, they agreed and signed the contract. It was a great chance for Charles, provided he didn't end up with a swollen head. To me he didn't seem the sort of child who would be bothered with fame or stardom; he seemed far too practical and down to earth for that.

Although I ended up as company vet I was originally asked to join for only ten days to help 'break' Charles in. I looked forward to it, yet wondered if the atmosphere of this kind of film making would be anything like the days at Ealing Studios in England when I had worked as an 'extra' to earn some holiday money. Acting had always been my second choice of career; I loved good drama and the thrill of the stage, both as spectator and actor. I had been shocked and disillusioned by what I found on the set of *A Matter of Life and Death*, the film on which I had worked. The endless repetition of lines, of scenes, the lack of real lasting acting ability—or so it had seemed to me. I was told that this was the way it was done and that the final effect would be stunning (which in fact it was). Yet that make-believe world of films which I could not equate with stagecraft could never be my choice of existence, though the finished product on the screen was often unbelievably good.

I knew little Charles well and had included him in the last five of my thirteen programmes. Although my own series had not required real acting ability, concentration and interest in animals were absolute essentials. Charles had both, though I was a little frightened for him when I realized how big a part he was going to have to play as Samson.

141

Toni had also been asked to help. He was to tranquillize the wild animals to be used in the many animal sequences. He welcomed the chance to try a new tranquillizing compound on a number of captive animals, though he knew that his time on the film set would be limited. We did not expect to be working with the company for more than two weeks, but finally, counting emergencies, we were actually involved, off and on, for a total period no less than two hard experience-rich months!

The film venture began with a pre-conference party when the cast, producers and senior crew were introduced to the press. Toni and I, invited in some nebulous capacity, brought with us another member of the cast as newly engaged as 'Samson', in the person of 'Pilipili', which means 'pepper' in Swahili, and aptly described her temperament. She was a one-year-old Colobus monkey who, having been bottle-raised, identified herself entirely with the human race. We were asked to care for her whenever her guardians were away, and hugely enjoyed her affectionate, expressive personality, although we could not relax our vigilance of her for one single moment of the day—or night. She had a habit of dividing her time between the lounge plant, just in its new flush of growth, our bathroom fittings and the shoulders of unwary guests whom she paid the supreme compliment of neatly marking with her very personal signature. When she got out and up into a tree she was at her best, quite naturally. She fed on leaves for hours at a time, played with the dogs by enticing them to jump up to catch her tail, and had the unnerving habit of disappearing just when the real owners were about to return from safari to collect her.

In the end, after wreaking really extensive damage on their lavatory bowl, she was banished to the animal orphanage, but as there was no cage to house her at that time, the curator, Bobby Cade, was at a loss as to what to do with the delinquent. I put a proposition to him: if I could persuade the film company to include her in the cast—and I really did feel that no film about Africa was complete without a monkey—then they, in return, would build her a large and collapsible cage which would eventually go back to the orphanage to house her. Bobby agreed to this proposition and Pilipili was duly accepted as a member of the film team. What part she was to play at what point in the film remained to be seen. She had not been written into the script but this did not matter in the least, we discovered later. At the producer's discretion, a film script seems a very fluid arrangement and anything can be 'written in' or scored out at a moment's notice.

We kept Pilipili in her basket right through the cocktail party and through the first part of the introductions. When I released her for her presentation she was quite delighted, both with the cocktail snacks she received and the attentions she was getting from everyone. She was photographed with both John and Mary Mills and Hugh O'Brien, the male lead, and loved every minute of it. By the time she was returned to her basket she had stolen everyone's heart with her lip-smacking and vocal endearments, but rather disgraced herself by emitting a stream of real Colobus invective as soon as I closed the lid. If she liked John Mills and he liked her it would help a great deal, for she would almost certainly be part of his farmhouse *ménage* in the film. How she was going to be kept on a strict fruitless diet and controlled off the set was anybody's guess. As it turned out she really did have to be watched very carefully and in the end I pinned a notice on the cage entreating everyone to be sensible.

Coming from a high altitude habitat, Pilipili would enjoy the film location; we climbed from 5,000 to nearly 8,000 feet as we drove from Nairobi to Nanyuki, a very picturesque small town set in the foothills of Mount Kenya. The company certainly had chosen a beautiful site on which to film; I could not imagine anything more spectacular. We arrived at the Silver Beck Hotel, whose bar lies right across the Equator, just after lunch; the monkey, whose cage had not yet come, was hidden somewhere in the depths of our car. She had enormously enjoyed the trip—rather more than we had—for we felt the responsibility of carrying a film star very heavily. Unable to open any window for fear she might take a sudden leap out, we nevertheless had to release her *en route* for obvious reasons. Persuading her to return was often difficult and could reduce one to absolute despair, for although she usually allowed herself to be caught very readily, she could be the very devil to approach. She was far better with children than with adults and had taken exception to Toni right from the start only because, in self defence, he had tried out some of his very special aggressive monkey behaviour sounds on her. He had forgotten to cancel it out by lip-smacking and backing bottom approaches, or even by being polite, as monkeys are, and advancing upon her with his eyes directed sideways. Thus whenever he approached she would get into a panic and clutch firmly any part of me she found available at the time.

We had heard that there had been a near-fatal accident involving one of the eland before the film unit had reached location. It had been caused by carelessness, rather in the manner in which bears cause accidents in the Parks of America when a 'just one more titbit please, or I'll help myself' kind of sequence can cause someone to be scalped. A young man who was working for John Seago had been taming down a group of eland most successfully. He had reached the point where the female and sometimes the males took oranges freely from his hands whenever they were offered. Then one day the young assistant entered an enclosure which contained both a male and female eland. He had been warned against this, for to keep an eye on two rapier-horned animals is always difficult. The male, who probably also wanted an orange, approached horns down rather truculently, pinning the unfortunate victim against the fence. Without any obvious anger, he suddenly jerked forward his head and pushed his horns into his chest and abdomen; a slow-motion tragedy that could have ended in disaster. However, since the assistant was a strong, healthy, sinewy young man, he survived; I visited him in hospital and thought never to see him again, for he already looked as if touched by death. Two weeks after that he was back at work, even if only at half-mast, showing hardly a sign of his near-fatal experience.

Preech

A Natal Parks Ranger holding an immobilized Nyala antelope

The taming down of captured animals is very important—John Seago

Charles Malinda as Samson with the zebra foal in *Cowboy in Africa*

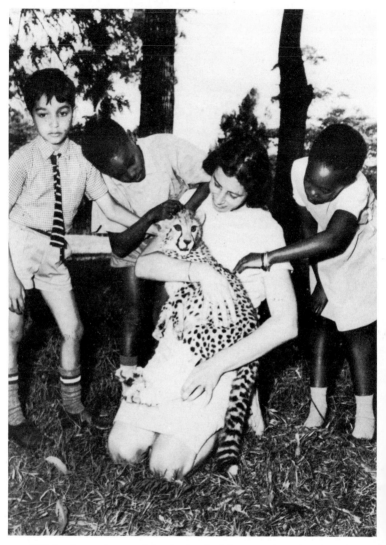

Briefly the author explained what had happened to the cheetah

Would this cast a gloom on the proceedings, were film people superstitious? Would other adversities follow? There were so many people and so many half-wild animals working on the set. Still, the country was beautiful and the work we were embarking on something new and exciting; part of a make-believe African adventure which *could* transmit a message to the millions, *if* Andy White's ideas materialized in the way we hoped they would. We both believed in what Ivan Tors was trying to do—if we had not, nothing on earth could have persuaded either of us to become part of his venture.

It was fortunate that our hostess, the thoughtful Mrs. Hook, whose family was as much part of the locality as was Mount Kenya, had insisted on giving us tea and biscuits when we arrived, late and after lunch though it had been. I needed all my energy the moment we reached the actual film location, about half an hour's drive across farmland away from the Silver Beck Hotel. The camera team, the producer and the 'inside' crew worked in a fenced enclosure. It had to be fenced, for somewhere along the line animals would be brought into the area from the nearby animal training and housing camp which the Seago-Parkinson team had constructed some weeks earlier.

It was all new to me; vehicles with mobile cameras covered with what looked like enormous tea-cosies, a man rushing back and forth with a blackboard which he somehow clicked just before and after each 'take'. A gentleman with a mobile wardrobe hovered in the background and the 'prop' man, with an immense stock of bits and pieces, scurried back and forth between his truck and the set. There was a lady cateress—one of the most efficient members of the company (locally employed), an assistant producer, and, in fact, an assistant everything. I supposed they all knew what they were doing and imagined that in time I would know too. For the moment I found it all terribly overwhelming and almost lost heart. We parked and gave Pilipili to one of the nurse's children; the monkey seemed to take to her at once, a great relief. That left us free to seek out Bundy Marton, who, having asked us to come that day, undoubtedly knew what it was he wanted us to do.

'The buckle scene, you've got to help. Charles isn't quite getting it,' he said, desperation in his voice. 'You're just in time.' Someone handed me a script, somewhat revised since I had last seen it, but that didn't matter since I remembered the 'buckle' scene very well. Toni, tall and aloof and seemingly disinterested in all the varied activities, was strolling about with an air of nonchalance.

'Oo's 'e?' I heard one cockney voice ask another. 'Blimey, he's tall as a bean pole. I hears someone say that 'e's to do with the animals, sort of vet like, but not really.'

Unknowingly, this member of the British crew really had hit the nail on the head, for, as I had always maintained, Toni was really too much of a scientist and not nearly down to earth enough to be called—as I was—just 'plain' vet. He was walking about the field with a proprietary air, hardly unbending when someone offered him a cup of steaming coffee. 'Lucky so-and-so,' I thought as I walked off with the forlorn-looking child starlet, 'wish someone would do that for me. Charles and I both need one.'

Together we worked through many heart-breaking scenes, heart-breaking for him for it was difficult for an untrained boy of ten to be suddenly turned loose into a world of film turmoil and painstaking, repetitive work. He did not have to memorize more than a few lines at a time, but even so the dramatic quality asked of him was hardly his to give. We went over and over and over the part where he had stolen the cowboy's buckle, had run away with it and had tripped on the dusty ground. He pitched himself after it and found that it no longer shone. Tears running down his face, the guilt-stricken boy begged the buckle not 'to die' on him, his breathless voice coming in jerky gasps. I was the guilt-stricken one! How could I ever have got my young friend Charles into this sort of pickle!

'Do it for me, for old time's sake,' I begged him. 'Try to really feel like a boy who is torn by sadness and by guilt and by not knowing where he belongs. Try, Charles,' I said, my

146

hands on his shoulders, 'and then we'll all be finished for the day.' Bundy and the rest of the team were sitting waiting for us to finish our own private rehearsals. I did the scene for him, inflected my voice the way I wanted him to, and tried to give him back some of his failing courage. 'Okay,' I called, 'this time he'll do it.' And after three 'takes' he did. That made it over twenty in all, which is a lot for a little boy who isn't an actor. In the end he was so frustrated by having to go on and on, even when we thought the scene was perfect, that he burst into tears and did just what he was meant to do: he portrayed an unhappy, confused child who was a victim of circumstance and who, more than anything in the world, wanted to make good.

I took him back and gave him milk and biscuits and tried to get him to unwind. We discussed people and films and I assured him that he would get used to the work and that in the end he would be proud, and his family too, of the part he had played not only for himself but also for Africa. While we talked an astounding fact revealed itself: during the whole week he had been there before me, no one had thought of reading the film script to him. Charles didn't know the story! No wonder he didn't understand what and who he was meant to be, and why he should look and act the way they wanted him to. We returned to the hotel with Toni and a few of the others and sat down and read it together. I told him about Andy White and how he had come to East Africa to see what it was really like before he wrote the story of the film. I explained that film producers had the sort of job which kept them busy all the time, so busy that it was hard for them to think of everything. I was sure that Bundy had already told him about the film right at the beginning in Nairobi, but then telling was never quite so thorough as reading. Now that he understood what it was all about, he could enjoy himself. He just had to pretend to be that Samson, ragamuffin turned into hero, whose dream, in the end, would come true.

That evening, long after Charles had gone to bed, we were still sitting over dinner with the directing team to decide on the next day's plan. Toni would not be needed and was getting a lift back to Nairobi; I would keep the car and stay 'on call'. The planning, I discovered that evening, could never be exact, for the weather, more than anything, was the decisive factor. Each moment had to be utilized, sun, shade or rain (which did come later too) and the scenes had to be shot according to climatic vagaries. Each day a working schedule was put out so that the team and stars knew what would be required; but it could change at a moment's notice, often to my chagrin.

Waiting was the most difficult part of my work. Hours when I wasn't needed, Charles not on the set, no animals in the scenes. I spent some of my time with Mary and John Mills whom I had never met before and who were absolutely charming. Not the temperamental playwright or film star, but a real, sincere, down-to-earth couple, utterly in love, never without each other unless it really could not be avoided. They adored the monkey and 'trained her in' for the scenes; it had to get used to being and staying near John. They genuinely loved animals and understood my heartache when I found, to my immense surprise, that in this film, which seemed to me to be about animals, they were used as 'props' instead of stars!

The Seago-Parkinson camp wasn't very far away. A few minutes across the fields and through a little gate and one had reached it. Thelma, Tony Parkinson's wife, was there too with her small brood and kept the home fires burning most wonderfully. It was a tented camp with an open kitchen and a 'down by the river is a path' choo; wild, yet homely and a pleasure to come to when the film activities across the way had reached a state of frenzy: the truck would not roll over and catch fire, the hero obstinately refused to be 'produced'. The villain didn't want to suffer the ignominy of being beaten by the hero, the heroine, having caught a sore throat, was out of sorts. The scientist had become listless and felt neglected, the assistant producer belligerent. The producer who had suffered for as long as he could stand it finally threw his hat on the ground and blew his top, which had a most salutary if only temporary effect on the cast.

I had found my first day, and indeed most of those that followed, very bewildering. Making a film really wasn't my cup of tea; it needed a special kind of *sang froid* personality with plenty of imagination and bordering on stoicism. There was no apparent sequence in the filming of the scenes, some of those towards the end being filmed first and vice versa. My own part of the animal work began on the second day; the gazelle were needed and the scene was the one for which we had been responsible in the first place. Tony Parkinson, John Seago's partner trapper and animal trainer, proved to be a joy to work with. We both had one main object in mind: *the animals came first*. He and John Seago had the same philosophy and the same code of ethics: if animals are to be 'used' by humanity, be it in zoos or in films or any other way, they must be protected at all costs. Every part of the process, from capture to delivery, must be humane and well-planned. There is no need for the animals to suffer—yet so very often they do!

John Seago, who had been pronounced an incurable tuber-culosis sufferer twenty years before, had come to Africa in search of high altitude, a better climate and tension-, fume- and smoke-free open-air life. Kenya had attracted him and so he had chosen it above all other countries. He just came, met people, found great kindness and stayed. Gradually he became agent and buyer of wild animals for the London and Whip-snade zoos, simply because there was need for one. When he saw the terrible state of the animals he had bought he decided to enter the trapping business himself and try to clean it up from the inside. His maxim, *'what you take on do well,'* certainly bore fruit within a few years, for by example he proved that wild animal trapping need not be a cruel form of animal exploitation. He did not just go out and catch at random; he began by studying the area, deciding where the animal could be caught most easily; then persuaded it to move there. If, after a few minutes of chase the truck had not caught up with its quarry, it was always abandoned and the chase not renewed. When they were caught they were brought to the home base in Nairobi and kept there from three to five months. This allowed mental as well as physical adaptation to take place and gave John a chance to rid them of internal parasites. The taming down of captured animals is a very important phase of capture—it often spells the difference between life and death. Not necessarily at the time, but during and after arrival, for the stress of travel and new surroundings takes a great toll, both mentally and physically.

In 1953 Tony Parkinson, whom John had known since he was a boy, came to join him in the trapping business and together they formed a wonderful combine. John's secret of success also had another basis: he had built up a group of men that worked as a team, irrespective of origin and colour, with whom he communicated with great ease. He communicated by example, and showed what animal-human relationship really means and can mean to the African who was inclined to regard an animal as so much 'meat'. When finally one of his assistants told him that he had discovered that animals could be one's friends, John knew that he had succeeded. Slight, almost gnome-like, but of exceptional charm of manner, his humour, common sense, humility and love of animals have made him and his team an example to the whole world.

Tony Parkinson had brought four Thompson's gazelle to the 'set' for me to tranquillize. Having received my instructions from home by telephone the night before, I knew how to work out the amount of drug to inject by weight. It was a new substance, new in the sense that Toni had not used it often before, but thought it would be ideal for this special purpose when depth of sedation had to be graded.

For the sake of research, which, as far as we were concerned, was how we regarded this project, I kept accurate notes of all drug reactions—that is, if I had a spare hand to put to paper. I would be carrying one gazelle on to the scene, one just sedated sufficiently so that it could lift its head but not take flight. Meanwhile another gazelle had to be prepared, this time more deeply so that I could place a plaster of paris cast round its 'injured' leg. Just as Tony Parkinson and I were congratulating ourselves on the success of our excellent split-second timing and waited for the 'shooting' to begin, a huge black cloud came drifting by—and then another and another. Before we could bat an eyelid, orders would be shouted in all directions, cameras moved, another scene prepared. 'We'll come back to it,' the inimitable Bundy would say crisply, 'keep them there.'

Within half an hour the gazelle were up and about, no longer in that 'perfect' state which was needed. We were loath to inject one animal twice in one day in case it caused complications. The number of 'Tommies' available after days and weeks of frustrating, head-spinning, dizzy-making film turbulence were not many, for the change in climate had exposed them to lung infection which had to be carefully treated and guarded against. An animal under too much stress is the first to fall victim to any illness; though the Seago-Parkinson outfit had been hired especially for the film, they had no intention of needlessly risking even one life.

'The play's the thing,' my dramatic coach and producer used to say to me in the days when the stage was my aim. But was the film the 'thing'? Was it really necessary to override the needs of animals? Bundy Marton, who had produced many wonderful film sequences in his day, loved animals too. Yet to him they had to serve and subserve; the actors could—and did —get hurt, and the animal 'stars' had to toe the line too. Toni, who frequently prevented me from walking out altogether, was, nevertheless, in his own imperturbable way, just as exasperated as I was. One day, when the changes of plan had been even more than usually capricious, he declaimed emphatically to anyone who cared to listen that they were treating the antelope as if they were animals!

In the following weeks I had resigned myself to the prolonging of our trials for the simple reason that the work had to be done. Toni and I tranquillized in various strengths and for various requirements, wildebeest, eland, hartebeest, different sorts of gazelle, zebra and rhino. The film horses got sick, and though they were cared for most efficiently they did need some extra veterinary attention. Eland and gazelle needed treatment, and even the little Pilipili, who acted her scene so well, was given a banana by mistake and almost died.

In the scene where the villain shoots an animal, Ivan decided that it was not to be actually killed. It had, therefore, to be sedated so heavily that it passed for dead; which was successfully done except that the large and sensitive ears twitched irrepressibly whenever they were touched! The little zebra foal which Samson had to feed and rope and ride had to be tranquillized too since it had a hefty back-kick for anyone but its family, in whose house many of the scenes were shot.

Toni's genius at inventiveness and his incredible ability of knowing just what was required were essential factors in the making of this film. The quarter-horses had to catch up with wildebeest to be roped; under the influence of drugs, they cut down their speed so that the horses could overtake them. Animals, when chased, suffer a great deal; when slightly sedated, they showed much less ill-effect.

As the film script demanded, many wild animals of different species were thus roped, captured and brought back to the farm by the two cowboys who had to work relentlessly to meet their dead-line. The villain, however, who did not believe in this new kind of ranching, released the herds in the dead of night, certain that he had successfully wrecked the venture.

But the animals came back; with gentle guidance they allowed themselves to be herded into the corrals where they knew that food, water and sanctuary awaited them. It was like something out of the Bible; gone were fear and apprehension, the barriers between man and beast. The scene contained a dream-like, almost fairy-tale quality that made one want to rub one's eyes in disbelief.

Did the onlookers on the set, did the audiences of the world realize just how such a sequence was made possible in the first place?

Nothing was faked, for the Parkinson team had worked for weeks and months, had patiently and with amazing skill trained the animals, many of them newly caught, to move from point to point across the fields and bush in harmony with man.

The original filming schedule, which had allowed only six weeks for the main scenes, both in Nanyuki and other locations such as Samburu National Park, was overrunning its time. This, I was told, was not unusual, though Bundy Marton was a past-master at keeping to plan. He drove himself relentlessly through the long days and weeks, though not by any means a young man nor endowed with good health. He had loved Africa since the days when he filmed the classic Watutsi dance in the film *King Solomon's Mines*, which won world acclaim. He knew and remembered many Kenya personalities, knew many places which he revisited, whenever he could, at weekends. His dream was to buy a piece of land in the Rift Valley and to live there with his charming wife.

'Four weeks to go and no rhino,' he fumed one night. 'We need it bad and we need it now. Where is it?' That was a typical Bundy explosion, and end-of-the-day anxiety symptom. Johnny Pellatt, his associate producer was doing his utmost. He had to mediate, organize and retrieve difficult situations as they arose with the British, very 'five o'clock is knocking off time' crew. He had to decide on extra pay, rules on the set, what to do with children who shouldn't be there, rush back to Nairobi to sort out difficulties with officialdom. He had succeeded in every respect—but—there was still no rhino. The Kenya Game Department had undertaken to supply the film unit with one by a certain date. The wild animal capture team had been try-ing to fulfil the agreement but had not been successful. The situation was getting desperate, for each day extra cost the company a small fortune. At last the Chief Game Warden asked Toni if he would come to their aid; he said yes, he would try, together with the Seago team. He was reluctant, for the area to which they had been assigned was not an easy one. On the edge of the northern frontier, beyond Isiolo, the terrain was a tangle of rock and thorn bush. The 'black' rhinoceros were hunted, poached, and hence wary and aggressive. Ordinarily any such venture would have been preceded by certain investi-gations. The reaction of the species to the drug, varying under different climatic and nutritional conditions, had to be taken nto account. The consequent state of health and temperament of the species were factors which Toni would normally have tried to determine before the real operation began.

As it was, the local Game Department representative in the person of Bill Winter, Game Warden, Nanyuki, acted as guide and adviser, proving, in fact, an invaluable and vital part of the team.

I did not join the first expedition, but waited anxiously for news on set, continuing, with Charles Malinda and the veterinary work, both treatment and tranquillization. At last the team returned, hungry and quite exhausted, disappointed but not defeated. Toni thought they could well have darted and captured a rhino on the very first day and at the first try. As they sighted a rhino entrenched in dense bush, and having crept within twenty yards, an ideal darting distance, something suddenly alerted it so that it charged straight through the tangle of thorns, narrowly missing the cameraman who dived headlong into a dense thicket in which he became inextricably tangled. Trying to discover the cause for the sudden alarm, they found a party of 'rubbernecks', who had climbed a tree, upwind of the rhino. Toni left the rest to my imagination, but I gathered that Bill Winter, ordinarily a mild and kindly man, had, on discovering the cause of their failure, burst forth with an amazingly comprehensive stream of blasphemy. That had been the end. They didn't manage to locate another rhino in workable conditions. 'All right, we'll go again,' the team promised. 'Just a few days of respite, refuelling and reorganization.'

'It is more than just a necessity, it is a challenge,' said Johnny Pellatt, and fortunately everyone took it in the same spirit. Bill Winter, already greatly behind with his work, Toni who was driving back and forth to Nairobi and who was getting more gaunt-looking every day, the Parkinson combine who were hard put to keep their vehicles on the road and had also to care for their animals on location. In the end I was asked to come along, mainly as nurse, and give any help if needed. I already knew that rhino flushing in that area was particularly dangerous; I preferred to be part of it rather than away, waiting to hear the outcome. Nothing was worse, as Tony Parkinson's wife, Thelma, sadly agreed, than to wait at home for the men.

We left Nanyuki at dusk. The rest of the team had already gone earlier, but we had waited behind for a friend who was to get a lift to Meru from Isiolo. We had only to drive fifty miles but it took several hours. The road, once the tar had ended, was full of ruts and corrugations, winding down and towards the mountain scenery, hazy with dust at sunset. It was downhill all the way from the high mountains; down into the hot country still containing the bandit 'shifta', whose tactics had forced the government to impose a curfew on the whole belt of frontier land. This was the home not only of the solitary, morose black rhinoceros but also of a host of other animals and beautiful birds. We reached our destination in the dark and slept the sleep of the just in the local warden's house, ready to rise at four the next morning.

I had never seen such a sight as the hour before dawn in that stark desert country. Looking east from the warden's house, bizarre masses of basalt rock rose out of the earth, silhouetted against the lightening sky. Then, as the sun rose, the sky became crimson red, seeming to burn with an intensity of its own. I had heard of the desert sun and its special magic; it was not the sun I knew or had ever seen anywhere else in the world, for it had a mystic quality, a power that was almost too strong to bear. As I gazed, bewitched, neglecting my early morning duties, a wind came up from some secret place and began to stir the leaves in the tree above me. It seemed also to stir the sunrise; gently it peeled away the first layer so that the sky lightened into the pink and palest blue of early dawn. The spell was broken and the serious business of the day would have to begin.

Bill Winter and four askaris (game scouts), Simon Trevor the cameraman, who hoped to get a record of the rhino capture, John Seago and his team, Toni and I gathered in the village of Isiolo to pick up the Turkana trackers who were essential for our task. After driving some way into country where rhinoceros were found, we stopped and the trackers went out alone. We waited and while we did we drank our thermos coffee and ate strengthening chunks of bread and jam and talked of things which somehow went with rhino chase—the philosophy of life, and poetry, and as we did we watched the clouds being blown across the stippled, fleecy sky. The long grass, like a bright yellow sea driven in waves, stirred memories of Van Gogh. How he had loved these yellows against blue, had welded them into one living, moving, churning symphony of life.

At last the trackers returned. They had spotted a rhino and guided our vehicles to the nearest place from which to approach. Here I was left while the rest, all except the Turkana in the big truck, went on foot to pinpoint the rhino's exact position. After their return they decided to move up the truck so that they would be certain of keeping the darted rhino in sight in spite of the thick country. I watched from the top of the big lorry and after a time saw the rhino was on the move. Then they went out of sight and I was left in suspense, wondering what was happening beyond my line of vision. What seemed hours later I saw the Land-Rover was being driven towards me erratically and at great speed by one of the askaris. At once I was on the alert, ready for trouble. 'Someone is knocked down, but they have the rhino,' he said quite clearly as he leapt towards me, 'come quickly. No,' he added as he saw my look of horror, 'it is *not* your husband.' I drove off in our Jeep, very glad that my first-aid kit was in order for the gravest emergencies, hardly daring to envisage what I might find round the next corner.

John Seago, shaken and bruised, was sitting up, his face ashen grey, but smiling. I made him lie down in the shade while his story came tumbling forth; and out of the corner of my eye I saw Tony Parkinson and his assistant near the trussed-up rhino which seemed about to go down. I treated John for shock and dressed his injuries, hardly believing that this was all he had suffered. Once tossed by a rhino, few escape severe if not fatal injury and here he was, a man of nearly sixty, complaining of little except headache, a great thirst and an ache in his legs! Someone had made an open fire near by and was heating water over it. Someone else located a teapot and some tea and milk and sugar. While the rhino was being finally subdued, while Toni was watching its breathing rate and drug reaction, I was feeding John with sweet hot tea to restore his fluid balance. As soon as I could turn my attention to the others, I saw that they, too, were in need of some stimulating fluid, for all five looked abnormally pale and very shaken. They came in turn and took their cups and as they sipped I was able to put together what had happened.

The rhino, a large bull, had been darted but had not yet completely succumbed to the drug. To ensure its capture the trapping team had thrown a rope, with a log attached, over its head, which slowed it down till it stopped. John Seago not realizing that there was slack in the rope, hopped off the truck, complete with camera, and began to take a film from the front. Suddenly, with surprising speed for so large a creature, the rhino charged towards him. John turned and ran, his speed a snail's pace compared with the rhino. He fell, and as he did the rhino horn passed miraculously under his body, tossing him high into the air. As he cartwheeled down the rhino was ready to thrust again but Toni rushed towards him and pulled him away in a flash, preventing a second and perhaps fatal toss. Meanwhile Tony Parkinson and Mike, his assistant, had tightened the rope and made the rhino secure.

From then on all went well and smoothly. The rhino was hauled, amidst chants from the Turkana crew, into a crate weighing nearly a ton which was winched on to a large lorry. Toni and I rushed John into Nanyuki for a medical examination in case of internal injuries, and were most relieved that he had sustained nothing more than I had already found. Thelma Parkinson, waiting anxiously for news, was very relieved to see us. She fed us while we told her our day's adventures and finally, with blankets round our shoulders, we sat, waiting like Isolde for Tristan, for the rhino and team to arrive. Its enclosure was ready. At 10.30 p.m., the truck arrived. At midnight, after a marathon lamplight piece of teamwork, the rhino walked into its new pen, safe and sound.

Or so we thought.

By the morning the new two and a half thousand pound

member of the company, as if trying to achieve stardom by a show of violent, artistic temperament, was butting and ramming his precious horn against the side of the enclosure. The workmen and fence-builders seemed to have aroused him to unabated fury as they frantically tried to raise the height of the pen, which, made ready for a far smaller specimen, would not have contained him for very long.

Just as everyone in the district arrived to admire the rhino, he was doing his best to destroy the symbol of his film image, and by mid-day had achieved his aim; his most magnificent and anterior appendage lay discarded on the ground. That done, he calmed down and watched the distracted producer, assistant director and others tearing their hairs out one by one. A rhino without a horn wasn't in the script but it was much too late in the day to go and catch another one.

From an air of triumph and elation, the mood changed to one of acute depression until someone brightly suggested using a rubber horn. And why not? It had only to be moulded on the shape of the old and stuck on with something that would weld rubber to skin. Impossible though it sounded, they decided to try and by the time the 'falsie' was ready, the rhino was much more amenable to human contact. With bated breath we waited while the operation was performed and, wonder of wonders, it worked! The rhino, having had time to contemplate his half-empty nose seemed glad, once again, to have something to sight by. Would it stick on and stay stuck while the rhino performed its act of charging through the undergrowth after the cowboy? That now was the million-dollar question!

The gods were kind, and it worked. What was more, no one could have known the difference, least of all the audiences of the world who eventually saw it on the screen. He played his scene with magnificent ferociousness though he did, just once, falter and stop in utter surprise when his horn bent impotently back under the weight of a log as he tried to lift it.

When it was all over he was released back into the wild, this time into a protected Sanctuary, his rubber horn no longer needed, ready to begin growing a new and perhaps a bigger and better one.

We all dispersed in various directions; the film producer to the cutting room to put the film to order and, we hoped, to perform miracles of editing. The Seago-Parkinson team were able to return to their bevy of animals; the stars went home to recover from the turbulence of film-making. Charles Malinda went back to school and normality, and we returned home to our various duties, dull compared to the weeks of turmoil we had just been part of! The only one who remained on location was Bill Winter, who had helped out the film company for none than an inner reward, and whose patience and humour had been tried almost to breaking point. 'Never again,' we had heard him say, 'never again will I work for films.'

11 *Animal Ark*

'LOOK,' SAID DOLPH HARMSEN, facing the cameras, 'He's behaving exactly like the monkey.' His little son, barely two years old, was jumping up and down making ape gestures and sounds such as I had often seen Pilipili making when she met someone she wasn't sure of. 'You see,' the Canadian zoologist explained, 'before a human child grows into an intelligent person, he is just like a monkey. Slowly he evolves and ceases to be like his primitive forefathers; but by watching him a moment ago you could see quite clearly *who* his ancestors were!' The boy, surprised and absorbed by the Colobus bundle in his father's arms, had reacted exactly as we had hoped he would, his antics endorsing the truth of the evolutionary theory. His mother came across and led him away, while Pilipili, having just completed her first screen role, hopped back into my arms.

The children, who had been listening intently to what Doctor Dolph had to say, now came into their own for question-time was just beginning. I returned 'into camera' to start the ball rolling, and noticed with delight that the two boys were already competing for the microphone. Doctor Harmsen, who had illustrated the evolutionary process by means of spontaneous drawings on huge sheets of paper against a blackboard, braced himself for what was to come. Had there been another whole hour it would not have been enough, for he had stirred the children's and my imagination and curiosity to the utmost.

Iain Douglas-Hamilton's forest home

Jack Hopcraft holding Preech, one year old, looking at his
playmate, the baby steen buck

The cheetah after the operation, wearing plaster of Paris casts

Screws's litter-mate helped his recovery enormously

'Doctor Harmsen, do we all come from monkeys, or some more than others?' asked Nikhil, and I wondered how our evolution expert was going to sort that one out. In an adult conversation this might have led to a long exposition, but for children, one had to keep to the straight and narrow. Dolph had a wonderful way of translating the most complex facts into simple terms. I was sorry this was to be our last programme, for I would very much have liked him to appear again. He handled the questions superbly; his explanation of the advent of man, of the gradual change of reptile into bird, of the things in the sea 'that began to move and have life', of our place in the overall plan, were beautifully and clearly put and not at any time did anyone feel that he had tried to exclude the Divine or the teachings of the Bible. For a few unreasonable moments I tried not to see the clockwise flourishes of the cameraman whose job it was to 'wind it up.'

That meant only three more minutes and this time it also meant good-bye for good. *Animal Ark*, Number 13, was about to end.

Charles, Nikhil, Pilipili and I formed a close-knit group for the conclusion. Doctor Harmsen's treatment of the evolutionary theory had given me just the opening I needed to sum up our series in such a way that I could remind the viewers why *Animal Ark* had come into being in the first place. I explained that what Doctor Harmsen had told us would make us think more deeply about the wonders of the world, among them our own share of wonders, the wild animals of Africa. *Animal Ark* had shown some of the different kinds there are and some of their strange, marvellous and varied shapes and habits. If we learnt about them, we would grow to love them and that would make us want to care for them, which in turn will help them to survive. The world and Africa was learning more and more about wildlife; by the time the children had grown up they would know so very much more than we do, that is, provided the animals are protected and preserved. If they are not, then there will be nothing *to* learn about or look at; no wings in the sky, no fish in the sea. The world would be very dull, colourless and barren without them, especially without those animals that live in Africa.

My venture into the medium of television had begun on the day I had taken my first finished manuscript of a radio-play to the children's section of Voice of Kenya. There seemed not only to be a need for children's stories but also for children's television programmes locally made. I found myself ushered into the office of Morris Mwenda, controller of television, who seemed interested in my rather unconventional ideas on primary biological education. I wanted to get away from the adult studio presentation technique and venture into the out-of-doors, allowing animals and children to come in close contact with each other. The producer and cameramen would have to be ready for any contingency, for it would be the very spontaneity of the programmes which, I hoped, would hold the attention of the audience.

He took me to the viewing room and asked me to look at an English television programme, which at that time was showing in Kenya. It was named *Badger's Bend*, after a village in England and was the most hopelessly unsuitable material to use in Africa.

'Can you do better than that?' Morris Mwenda asked, when the lights went on again. 'Can you make something for children with local colour?'

'I'd like to try,' I answered. 'Give me your outdoor video unit, a crew and facilities. I'll find some children, animals and locations and give you a basic plan. But don't ask me for a script, because it's impossible. The children that will appear in my programmes must feel free and unrestricted.'

A well-meaning friend suggested that before I take the plunge into the unknown I might do well to consult a few of the wildlife personalities who were interested in education of the young.

'Maybe it's the high altitude,' he said kindly, 'but you will find people in East Africa just the slightest bit touchy. They seem to be possessed with an especially strong territorial instinct, maybe from watching too many wild animals. You're

162

new and I don't want you to get discouraged before you start. Whatever anyone says to you, give him the benefit of the doubt as to his motivation and don't get into arguments. Especially with the ones who have tried and have failed. Once you have made your contacts and courtesy calls, then there's nothing to stop you, and meanwhile you will have gained great insight into the intricacies of the conservationist, biologist and wildlife missionary mind, which is quite different from anything anywhere in the world!'

He was right but I enjoyed it. It was a humbling and also a very exhilarating experience. The nicest most outgoing people were at most tolerant and somewhat doubtful, others were horribly discouraging.

Finally, in my last week of visits, I sought out the newly arrived American wildlife officer who had been loaned to Kenya Parks by United States Parks. We had already met during our last days in Washington, D.C., and I thought then that Parks had made a wonderful choice. Rob Milne came to create an Educational Centre at the entrance of the Nairobi National Park. He knew just how to put ideas across to the young, how to lead them through his museum in such a way that they became part of its contents. Push a button here and a bird will appear, open the side of a tree and you will find what kind of animal normally lives inside. He combined these gimmicks with the unhappier side of wildlife education—the truth about poaching and needless killing. In spite of his own clear-cut mission he had also met with many adversities. No one could deny the value of an educational centre which would familiarize visitors to the Park with the animals and birds contained in it. Yet there were those who resented new ideas *because they were new*. Rob, and the African Wildlife Leadership Foundation representative, Frank Minot, both found this attitude bewildering and frustrating, but in the end, by sticking to their guns and refusing to give in, they won, and the educational centre came into being and into daily use.

Frank Minot, who officially administered the projects of the A.W.L.F. in the whole of East Africa, did not immediately accept me as 'one of the family'. Though he had known Toni off and on for years we had not met before and being the sort of man he was, he was not prepared to take me on face value just because Toni and I were married. Far from it! Endowed with well-based suspicion which stemmed from years of disappointment and disillusionment, he 'put me through the hoop', until I felt I really was being tested for a circus. His own integrity was such that he could not stomach anyone whose standards fell below his own. Was I genuine and sincere, that was his problem. When he discovered that our aims and objectives were identical, he emerged from his shell and gave me that extra spurt of courage I so badly needed.

'We are in a race between Catastrophe and Education,' he told me during one of our discussions. 'We from the West (he was an American) are here to help Africa keep safe its wildlife trust; make no mistake though, they are the trustees. Since 'Uhuru', the wildlife sanctuaries have grown in number. If the African can come to honour his heritage as the Eskimo came to honour the seal and the Red Indian the buffalo, African wildlife will be safe. Nothing can nurture the protective instinct more than the recognition of the basic values of that which needs protection.'

I had been advised to seek the co-operation, blessing and sponsorship of the Minister of Tourism and Wildlife, the Hon. Mr. Sam Ayodo, who had been a teacher, loved children, and might well give official support to the series. With trepidation I did so, wondering what sort of reception I would get. Jean Barton, his radiant and efficient secretary, had seen my look of nervousness as I was about to enter the office door. With a sweet smile and a word of encouragement, balancing two cups of steaming coffee in her hands at the same time, she ushered me in and introduced me in such a way as to dispel my apprehension and make me feel at ease.

I was amazed and delighted at the man behind the desk who welcomed me. However formidable he might have appeared to some, he certainly took off his cloak of ministerial officialdom after the first five minutes. Over a delicious cup of coffee I introduced my theme of direct approach to the African child and explained my findings during the last two weeks. The people I had met, consulted, and the resulting conclusions. He questioned and cross-examined me in his very special way, trying to gauge the real worth of the project, to examine its stability, to make certain that if he gave his name to it it would have to be something that he himself could be proud of.

'Yes, Doctor Sue,' he said in his deep bass voice, his striking face lighting up with a wide smile, 'I will support you but on one condition: when you have made your Number 1 programme I want to see it. If I pass it, then you may go ahead and I will be happy to introduce the whole series for you.'

I left, quite charmed by his genuine, disarming personality sensing his great love for wildlife which had been entrusted to him, and for children who were the essential key to its preservation.

Next time we met it was in the television studio for the screening of our No. 1 programme, which he and the Chief Game Warden passed as suitable. Now all that had to be done was to arrange for a time when his own introduction could be filmed and spliced on to *Animal Ark*, No. 1. Having him as official sponsor put the right touch to the series, for it gave continuity to the work we were all trying to achieve in different fields, work that *should* be united and co-ordinated, each step and stage a thread in the same weave.

Being endowed with an impatient nature, I now wanted to get to grips with the work in hand. I made my reports to Voice of Kenya, told them of the Minister's provisional sanction of the series, and proceeded to search for children who might be suitable participants within the programmes. First I had to decide on the sort of institution from which to draw my team. Orphanages, schools or privately? I needed children of reasonable intelligence, with good English diction and an interest in animals. They should be pleasant to look at and fairly well behaved. I wasn't looking for a model child; far from it. Yet I did want to avoid the kind that would stick a pin into the cheetah's tail at the most inopportune moment!

Luckily I had become a fair judge of child character, partly through my work in schools, partly through my 'junior assistants' in veterinary practice and because I had children of my own, which usually meant double or triple their number in and about our farm. I would still have to rely on the help of the headmasters and teachers, for they would have to make the initial selection of the groups.

I began by visiting Doctor Barnado's Homes for orphaned children. I spent some hours with the children on a completely informal basis, trying to gauge their standards, their interests and their personalities. I also visited schools and drew some of my children from these, though the more sophisticated school child was harder to judge at first impression. On one occasion, I chatted with twin African girls who, I thought, would be a great asset to our series. I asked them routine questions to put them at ease, including one about their own pets. 'I never keep any,' said one of the twosome, 'they give me such terrible nightmares.'

'Same here,' said the other, 'wild animals are the worst. I never want to see wild animals in the Park. They're dangerous!'

What a mistake it would have been to judge only on appearances; that sort of sentiment on the *Animal Ark* screen would have turned it into a fiasco, a sort of comedy 'take-off' on the value of wildlife. Eventually I chose a team of ten (far too many!) for our first 'fade-in' shooting in the Nairobi National Park. We needed a signature film and I thought that a scene in the animal orphanage would do the trick; for what could be more wonderful than the sight of children playing or even close to orphaned wild animals!

This pre-programme filming would also serve as a guide-line for our future work. For the first time we would be together as a unit. We hoped to learn more about the children: from behaviour pattern (which confused us utterly) to their trend of thought and interest. I had managed to find an assistant in the person of Dorothy Udall, wife of one of Toni's lend-lease American colleagues. Without her, *Animal Ark* would never have been completed; her calm stability in times of stress (which was often), her ability to gather elusive children from all corners of our film locations and transform them from hooligans into screen personalities, was nothing short of genius. She helped me to plan each programme and gather our team each week, which, on one occasion, included transport of one enchanting donkey foal from the depths of Kikuyuland. She made drawings to demonstrate relevant points, her veterinary knowledge a great asset. Above all, she kept me sane and gave me strength and comfort whenever I needed it, which, during the months of filming, was six days out of seven.

The Director of Parks, Mr. Perez Olindo, had given his permission for our work in the Park. The curator of the wild animal orphanage, Bobby Cade, had agreed to co-operate and advise us, for only he knew which animals could be safely approached. We began with the reticulated giraffe, a great favourite but nevertheless an eight-foot-high giant equipped with most efficient-looking hooves. As soon as the children beheld him, most of them having never seen one before, they simply swarmed all over him, making a point of investigating his nether regions as well as his black switch tail. As I hauled one child out so another appeared under the navel, but in the end, with Dorothy's help, we managed to extricate them and deliver a disciplinary lecture—the first of many to come.

Soon we had them happily settled on a high crate from which they could give the bottled milk formula which Bobby had brought just in the nick of time. At this point the cameraman was working overtime, for this was just the sort of 'fade-in' we envisaged. After that he filmed some of the children communicating with cheetah, round which they asked endless questions which gave me ideas of the sort of thing we were likely to meet later on. They did have to keep fairly still in the cheetah enclosure, which didn't amuse them at all, for above all, children between five and ten years of age hate staying in one position for more than one minute at a time. The cameraman who had, perhaps, also never visited the animal orphanage before seemed to have lost his head. Out of two hours of filming children and a variety of animals, not even three good usable minutes emerged, a great pity in view of the unique scenes which could have been recorded.

On the way out the children divided into two groups, something I had tried to avoid, and became, once again, almost unmanageable. The littlest boy, Jimmy, put his foot inside the wild-dog fence and almost lost some of his toes, the bevy of girls had sought to try the patience of the already over-harassed (ex-circus) bear by poking their fingers inside the wire mesh. The lions were growling fiercely at the bear-neighbour every time they met on the dividing line, perhaps competing for the first taste of children's finger. With Dorothy holding the fort on the wild-dog side, I rushed over to the lion-bear situation and have not to this day discovered how each child came away with the full complement of ten whole fingers. Guardian angels specially posted to the *Animal Ark* venture? By the time the whole series had been made I had no more doubt on the subject, for we escaped with one cut hand, which was due to something other than an animal cause.

From my initial contact with the children I concluded—and confirmed—my suspicions that the African child knows far less about wild African animals than the European. Perhaps, then, we should begin our series with some programmes about the domestic animal with which the Kenyan child was familiar. The cow, the donkey, the chicken, cat and dog had been part of their lives for generations. They represented their wealth, their form of protection and, most important, their sustenance.

For three consecutive Fridays we brought an agricultural training station to a standstill. The cameras and video unit had to be set up and connected to the electric current, the animals to be used had to be gathered into a central enclosure. They resented the disturbance of their routine, as do all creatures of habit, and though we expected some sort of protest from the manager and his staff, we found nothing but kindness. On the very first day, we suffered from wind disturbances and the passing of traffic as well as badly set cameras and lack of adequate direction, which did not contribute much to the success of our No. 1 programme. The cow kicked so hard at the microphone cable hidden in the grass that it came asunder and this meant a retake of the previous section. Since we were all in the experimental stage, the director asked us to start at the beginning as soon as the last word had been spoken, which contributed little to the spontaneity of the children's questions about the animal under discussion: the cow and calf.

Having asked once and received an answer, they understandably saw no sense in asking the same questions again. Dorothy, as always, came to the rescue and during the ensuing break explained the whys and wherefore of television technique in her wonderful, simple way. That seemed to imbue them with new enthusiasm, all except the littlest of the team, the starry-eyed Jimmy who could not bring himself to concentrate any longer and simply wandered off camera to admire something else at the other end of the field. Someone brought him back and induced him to enter the line of vision just as 'question time' was about to begin, which brought his attention back sharply to the business in hand.

He loved asking questions and was surprisingly good at keeping to the point. What he could not achieve was the pronunciation of my first name, transforming me from 'Doctor Sue' to 'Doctor Zoo', which many felt was a great improvement.

Having kept us on tenterhooks while we waited for his question, he became extremely distressed as he admitted, with tears in his eyes, that he had forgotten what it was he was about to ask. Meanwhile some of the others would chip in with their queries which, depending on the animal we were studying, dealt with such things as the mechanics of chewing the cud, whether animals suffered from corns, the love-life of cows and bulls, the psychology of the giraffe (put into very simple terms); the reason why a wildebeest could twitch its skin when we couldn't, the intricacies of milk production and

169

a host of other questions. Somewhere in the middle of them all, and while I tried my hardest to keep my crew in order and my face straight a small hand would tug at my sleeve and an even smaller voice would tell me that he now remembered what he had wanted to ask. Since he had not been listening to what had gone before, his question was often a repetition of someone else's, which caused a furore in the group and a loss of the precious minutes that were ticking by. We had only twenty in all and could happily have used sixty. By the time we had to wind up, the children's questions had really only just begun and quite often Dorothy and I remained behind to satisfy their curiosity.

This was just what we had hoped for: genuine interest and unrehearsed unselfconscious probing into the world of animals. When we watched our programmes on Sunday evening, usually surrounded by a group of children to judge their reactions, we noticed that they enjoyed the moments of imperfection more than anything else: when the puppy nearly chewed the cord to bits, when the baby rhinoceros got her legs tangled in the cable so that I had to unravel it, bottom up. They laughed uproariously when the half-wild serval cat, which Dennis Kearney had brought from the Nairobi Park to compare with a series of domestic cats, bit his shoulder just as he was praising its amiability. Through laughter and imperfection, through trial and error, we reached a higher standard week by week. I chose different children for different programmes and found that the slightly older boy balanced a girl who was a year or so younger. On the whole the cameras did not affect the children once their interest had been aroused; they seemed to forget their presence just as much as we did. We changed locations—and producers—but on the whole the crew remained the same. Our fourth programme dealt with the domestic fowl which is very much a part of East Africa's rural life. Through meticulous and careful planning (or so we thought), and with the help of the manageress of Kikwaru Poulty Farm, we had set our filming date on the very afternoon of the morning that a batch of eggs was due to hatch out from under the most flamboyant of the bantams. As we arrived, the lady met us in the drive-way, much distressed, and explained that something had gone terribly wrong with the chick routine. 'We're finished,' she said in broken English, 'no babies.'

The children, Dorothy and I put our heads together and talked it over. Although the programme would contain an immense amount of other material, the actual hatching would have been a highlight. 'Have you any empty newly broken shells?' Dorothy inquired, her ingenuity in times of emergency saving the day yet once again. 'We'll fake it. We'll put one of your youngest chicks in a shell which will be almost as good as seeing it break through.'

The children thought this was hilarious, for never before had we attempted to hoodwink the audience by 'rigging' a scene. Jimmy would be the one to discover the newly hatching chick as the hen got off her nest and would pick it up as it began to break through. But the four-day-old chick was a little large for the shell and collapsed through the wrong end tail first from sheer overweight and oversize. In our enthusiasm we had forgotten to dampen the chick and fervently prayed that no one would detect how fluffy and dry it looked. When the final product was shown months later it looked amazingly realistic, the best part of it being the expression on Jimmy's face as the chick disappeared backwards and out of view.

We moved from a poultry farm to a cattery, then to the home of a lady who kept over seventy dogs of different breeds in wonderful harmony with each other. We were able to make a unique programme at her home, for she owned breeds ranging from champion Great Danes to Chihuahuas. She also had sick dogs under her care, which delighted me, for I was able to demonstrate the value of treatment versus untimely destruction.

There was always so much to say, to teach, to answer, and so little time to do it in. Retakes became more and more infrequent as teamwork and technique improved. Instead of spending from two until nearly 7 p.m. on one twenty-minute programme (including the hours the producer sometimes kept us waiting), we now finished just after tea-time. That made it possible to take a break, have tea and look at animals, small reward for the children before they had to be rushed back to their schools or residences.

Once we began the wild animal part of the series they enjoyed it more. How many children anywhere in the world had ever seen a baby elephant, or a baby rhino for that matter, at close quarters? Naturally they were envied by their friends, some of whom wrote to ask if they could also take part in *Animal Ark*, and sometimes this was possible. But the glamour of getting close to a wild animal was in itself fraught with danger, for we did not want to give the impression that they would make safe playmates under any circumstances! It had to be explained, firmly and clearly, that these were special animals and special conditions which had been created so that people and children could learn about them more fully. Even here in the animal orphanage we had to be very careful; wild animals, even though raised by human foster-parents, such as the rhino had been, were still apt to revert to their instinctive pattern of aggression. They might not intend to cause harm but when a small boy got in the way of a giraffe hoof the result might be loud and painful.

The group I had chosen on the day of the cheetah programme was composed of three children. One girl and two boys, just enough to keep an eye on. Since I was still practising with wild animals I had no difficulty in finding wild animal subjects. The two cheetah cubs had come to the Nairobi National Park from the Aberdare mountain area, cared for by the Warden of the Aberdare Mountain National Park and his wife, Billy and Ruth Woodley who, for years, had lovingly nursed and often rescued injured, stray and orphaned wild animals. On one of our lightning trips to Meru we had been diverted by radio telephone at the last moment for they wanted us to touch down to see a sick cheetah.

'We'll almost certainly be bringing one cheetah back to Nairobi,' we told the unhappy pilot. 'You won't mind, will you?'

'How big is it?' he wanted to know. 'Will it fit into the spare seat?'

'No, I don't think so,' Toni said, deadly serious, though he knew full well from the call that the cheetah was not yet four months old. 'We can drape it across the back and hold it down, maybe even give it a tranquillizer.'

'I hear it has a badly upset stomach,' I said, most unwisely, for that seemed to have put the final touch to the pilot's mounting distress.

Ted Goss's wife, Else, who was getting a lift from Meru to some friends who lived near the Woodleys, tapped the pilot on the shoulder. 'Hey,' she said with her best ex-air hostess personality. 'You're not flying the shortest way!' Toni and I looked at each other dumbly, two minds with but one thought. Mount Kenya seemed to be on the wrong side of the wings but since we had never flown to the Aberdares we couldn't be sure. But Else was. With amazing accuracy she guided the shamefaced pilot to our destination. I tried my hardest to cheer him up while we waited for the Woodleys to arrive on the strip and I felt for the first time a deep sympathy for his distress. After all, a pilot can hardly be expected to keep his sense of direction with the prospect of one large, ill, uncontrollable cheetah hanging over his head!

The cheetah cub was not well but not ill enough to warrant an air journey to Nairobi. He and his litter-mate would be brought down in a few days and meanwhile we left medicaments for his treatment. After an hour we had to leave the Woodleys' glorious mountain home, for the afternoon was almost over and take-off could not be delayed. We promised to return soon and stay longer. One could get quite lost in vistas of forest, mountain and mist, 3,000 feet above Nairobi. The Woodley children were pink-cheeked and vigorous, the adults full of high altitude energy. The air was like champagne, pure as crystal, and when one took a deep breath it really did go to one's head. There were many places in the world where I would have liked to spend weeks, months and years, and this was one of them. Africa was beautiful, whichever way one

173

looked; it would require several hundred lifetimes to become part of each different heaven.

Some weeks later, when the cheetah brothers had been duly installed in the animal orphanage as new residents, I received a very urgent call from Bobby Cade. There had been an accident, a bad one, involving one of the cheetah, and could I please come at once? It took me twenty minutes to get to the Park and another three to reach the cheetah pen. Bobby was standing in the parking area, ready to guide me down with long fast steps, using those moments to give me the case history. One of the chimps had escaped from her enclosure at feeding time and had decided to invade the cheetahs' privacy. She had landed on top of their wire-covered run and as she did so, undoubtedly without any evil intentions, but with terrific impact, had caused one of the cheetahs to leap back with fright, injuring himself very severely. The other cheetah, more placid, had not reacted to the chimpanzee at all, and when I arrived they were sitting next to each other, one purring loudly while the other showed visible signs of distress.

The poor animal was hamstrung! He could not move his hindlegs off the ground since both his 'heel' bones (os calcis) had been broken. By careful palpation I discovered that there were fractures, though I could not confirm their extent nor their exact location without the help of X-rays. I called Toni and consulted with him and we decided that we would take the cheetah to the Veterinary Clinic as soon as possible. 'Do you think it is worth it?' said Bobby. He was a very kind old man with years of experience of animal work behind him. Nothing was ever too much trouble, yet the sight of the cheetah in such a pitiable condition made him lose hope just a little. 'Cheetah bones are so fine, so brittle . . . would they ever heal?' It was a good question, for we had found the cheetah bone structure seemingly most inadequate for its needs. Climbing trees and catapulting down made little sense when limbs were not constructed for severe concussion.

'Let's have a try,' I suggested, 'the X-ray will give us a clue. We can decide after we have seen them,' Carefully we lifted the cheetah up and placed it into a grass-filled box with movable side doors. Toni had made an appointment for the X-ray and we didn't want to waste any time. The cheetah had to be heavily sedated for a good picture and after that the vets at the College clinic and we would put our heads together and decide what to do.

It was as we had feared; both heel bones were broken off but fortunately not shattered. The growing bones had responded to the sudden impact and the simultaneous tension of the Achilles tendon with a clean snap. The bone fragments were still attached to tendon and under sedation their separated ends could be felt quite clearly. 'It's a job for an expert,' was the consensus of opinion. 'There is no one in East Africa who can tackle such a specialist orthopaedic job.'

That gave me an idea. 'Let's find a human orthopaedic surgeon to do the job. Perhaps one that is interested in wild animals.'

With no time to waste, I telephoned an ophthalmic surgeon who had shown great interest when I had told him about George Adamson's lion's eye. Perhaps he would help us to find someone, even at such a late hour. 'Of course I understand the urgency,' Doctor Bisley answered my strange request as if surgery on a cheetah's legs was an everyday affair. 'Get on to Doctor Griffiths from Glasgow who is a top man, he might help you.'

And so it was arranged. Doctor Griffiths showed enthusiasm as well as interest and agreed, after examining the cheetah and the X-rays, to operate at the veterinary hospital clinic. It was a combined effort. Toni and I administered the sedation and anaesthetic, the vet on duty helped with the operation. We all watched and learned a great deal. To see the expertise of a skilled human surgeon meeting brittle cheetah bones for the first time in his life was something of an experience. His first step had been to select two thin stainless steel screws. He cut through the tissues and exposed the heel bone, then drilled a hole through its length with his special surgical drill. By inserting the screws into the newly drilled hole he firmly anchored the fragment of the heel back on to its base. After resuturing the tissues he calmly repeated the operation on the other leg.

How marvellous it was to be so at home in one field, how much more preferable to our 'jack of all trades' call of life which lacked, as yet, in specialization.

The operation was a great success. Plaster of Paris casts were put on both sides for additional support and post-operative therapy administered. We took the cheetah home and put him next to the warming cupboard in the bathroom. We got up every hour to see how anaesthetic recovery was progressing and gave fluids to counteract shock and dehydration. Knowing how badly cheetah take deep anaesthetization, we worried a great deal and for a few hours almost lost heart. Then, at 3 a.m., I heard the most wonderful sound in the world—the loud, rolling purr of the awakening cheetah. Within eight hours he was moving quite strongly and by that afternoon we were confident of complete recovery. The Kearneys in the Park had agreed to take the convalescing patient, having made a special enclosure to house the two litter-mates together. This, in spite of all our doubts, worked like a miracle. Contrary to expectation, the uninjured brother did not interfere with his white bandaged sib, aptly named 'Screws', but aided his recovery enormously. Being together prevented the lassitude and depression so often evident in injured and sick wild animals and after some months, during which Screws was regularly X-rayed to check the position of the joints, he showed immense progress and a renewed feeling of independence.

First the casts were removed. More X-rays, and a few days of breathless waiting. Would the embedded screws really take the weight? Would the bones retain their union? Doctor Griffiths carefully followed the progress of his patient and delighted in the success of his unusual piece of surgery. The stainless steel screws would remain in place for life; by the time his term of office in Kenya was up and he had to return to Glasgow, the cheetah was walking almost normally.

Animal Ark, last but one, No. 12, was our cheetah programme. As often as possible I had invited a warden or biologist or animal expert to join us and to provide some of the answers for the children's questions. This time I had asked Billy Woodley to come and talk about wild cats and National Parks, for I thought the time had come when our viewers would want to know where each kind of wild animal was to be found and protected. I took only five minutes of time with an initial brief outline of the basic features of a cheetah. Screws was there, then still in his snow-white casts (which had been renewed several time to keep pace with the young animal's rapid growth), and I explained in a few words what had happened to him. I told of the operation and why it had been performed in the first place—and by whom. 'A people's doctor,' they said, wide-eyed. 'We didn't know THEY treated animals.'

'Why not?' I replied, and the discussion far outlasted the programme itself. 'Why cannot all sorts of doctors get together and share their work? Animals and humans have bodies with many things in common; much of what we know about animals and their sicknesses we have learnt through the pioneering work on man.'

If only we had more time together! We had studied five domestic species and antelope, elephant, rhino, cheetah, had even made two giraffe programmes in the rain. *Animal Ark* was only a small beginning but it did prove that young children in Africa as everywhere else, do have an insatiable interest in the animal world.

If they meet that world on their own level it does not seem too vast or too remote for them to enter. It is their world after all, but they must be made aware of it.

Our series had been the first of its kind made locally for local needs. It was hoped that it would reach many children in outlying districts by means of mobile film units and that their reactions, as well as those of our city and town audiences, would be assessed before we continued our work. Our measure of success—or failure—could only be judged by the children themselves; already we were aware of many of our imperfections and shortcomings. Our next *Animal Ark* series would have to reach a much higher standard, but at least we had made a start—and, contrary to the predictions of so many, had survived!

12 *Tinker Bell the Rhino*

THE RAINY SEASON had begun just as *Animal Ark* ended and I could now settle down to other work and perhaps to plan a new series for the following year. I was delighted to see the parched vegetation revive; so were the farmers, the game wardens and even some of the biologists, depending on what they were studying. If it were a matter of following lions, such as George Schaller was doing in the Serengeti, and they, in turn, were following the herds who sought shelter in the forests, then there would be little rejoicing about early rains. They disrupted Toni's experiment, too, for his radio-telemetry on eland was, at this time, specifically aimed at measuring their response to solar radiation (in simple terms: sunshine), and this meant no more work would be done until it cleared. As no one knew whether the rains were an unseasonal extra burst, perhaps to make up for the lack of rain the month before, or an early beginning of the rains which should come the following month, it made planning difficult.

Some biologists, studying wild animals less disturbed by rain, enjoyed it. The overall benefit to the wild herds was tremendous, especially to the grass feeders. It meant that there would be plenty of milk for the newly dropped calves. The young wildebeest began to run almost as soon as they entered the world; they had to, or perish. There was so much to run away from, for in the wake of the large herds the predators were at the ever-ready. Good rains meant plenty of colostrum (first milk), without which they had even less chance of survival.

Tourists decried the early rains. They had a planned schedule, hated to get wet or, worse still, bogged down. They didn't feel particularly lyrical about the sight of dripping, wet-skinned animals, nor did they find them good subjects for photography. Lions and leopard were elusive, the well-known waterholes not frequented since water was now dispersed. I condoled with Toni, even tried to cheer him up, for being happy alone is never much fun. I rejoiced when the rain began to fall, for to me the smell of new-wet earth was sheer heaven. I had to admit that a city never looked good when it was wet; it became drab and messy and slippery. People became over-heated in raincoats and poked each other in the eye with umbrellas. They became ill-tempered, contracted colds and sore throats and grumbled more than usual. When the sky turned grey they denounced the weather. When it turned blue again they felt just as bad but didn't know where to lay the blame. There was only one thing to do, and living in Nairobi made it very easy: to get out of the city. Wherever one lived it could hardly take more than fifteen minutes to reach the city limits, away from pavements and traffic lights, the overfull parking lots, the unruly rush-hour queues and the screech of wet brakes. One could not always escape, that was true, but even so the weekend was never more than five days away.

I had a date with my favourite biologist on one of those early February mornings. The rain had washed my car a shining blue but had also turned our drive into the beginnings of a mud-trap. I opened the windows and let the early morning dampness envelop me, nostalgic for my old farm-home and the sight of the potato tree in full blossom, in three shades of mauve, glistening and dripping after the rain. I had seen it change and grow through many seasons, never bare of colour, and had somehow thought that it would always be there—in front of my window with me to look at it. That was exactly when Fate scooped me up out of my complacency and put me down in the most unlikely place before I had time to orientate myself. Sometimes, as though jet-propelled, I found myself waking in a strange bed in a strange place—with a strange man!—too sleep-ridden to understand how I had got there, my subconscious not yet fully aware or able to cope with the many journeys and changes that I had undergone. When it was fine I lived entirely in the present, when the rains came I became restless. Memories, more like textures and scents and sounds rather than actual remembrances came flooding back and the old homesickness returned. Hard to explain to a new husband who wanted, above all, to cut off the past in which he had played no part. He also knew that the memories would *not* fade as time went on, but would become more vivid. I wanted to share them with him, for they were like old friends; if I were patient enough those old friends would one day join the new until we would hardly know the difference.

My family, somewhat slower rhythmed on that cold, dark morning, were loath to stir into life. I made the children's school lunch, kissed them each in turn and went out of the front door just as the incredibly long green Land-Rover rounded the corner of our driveway. No one had believed that he would really come, but then they didn't know Bristol Foster, who loved the feeling of the soft wet earth under the wheels (secure in his four-wheel overdrive) and the lack of dust in his nostrils. He had been conducting giraffe research, a study over four years involving 250 giraffe, some resident, some coming and going in the Nairobi National Park, an area of forty square miles.

He had been tracking them by means of radio-transmitting collars, had photographed every one of the 250 he had seen; had watched their behaviour, found a method of 'neck pattern' identification and come to know a great deal about their lives and their habits. It was always delightful to be with Bristol. He was so utterly dedicated to his work, yet still had time for his friends and time to share his knowledge and his findings. Boyish-faced, yet with slightly greying, receding hairline, he was, at thirty-five, a biologist who could rise to the very top of his profession, had he wanted to. But he didn't, not if it involved competition and perhaps personal strife, the too careful planning of the steps to the top. He was carefree, rejoiced in his work, a good teacher, an amusing companion and devoted family man.

When I asked him if he had sprung from a long line of biologists he denied it. 'I am a mutation. None of my family have ever been the slightest bit interested.' Bristol had wanted to become an ornithologist, but since the only kind of '-ologist' his father had ever known to make a decent, dignified living had been a geologist, it looked as if Foster junior would also be steered that way.

But geology didn't attract him. He had seen East Africa and returned to it, this time with a biologist wife who was a superb cook, artist and photographer. When I asked him what he thought of giraffe, he surprisingly answered: 'They are long and scrawny, like Toni'—who was sprawled out next to him— 'and me.' Most true! He did admit that the reticulated giraffe were beautiful, but those were not the ones he studied. They were not to be found in the Nairobi Park at all.

Bristol had been one of my visiting scientists in *Animal Ark*, one who had given me not only help but a lot of encouragement and faith. That had meant a great deal. I had been so new in Kenya and he, though a Canadian who had come only two years before me, somehow had most people and situations summed up and was always at my elbow when I needed advice.

After barely fifteen minutes' drive we reached the Mombasa Road gate, signed the non-paying honorary entrants' book, and went through. In spite of the few inches of newly fallen rain, it was easy to see that a long period of dryness had gone before. The Park still looked brown-yellow, yet if one looked very carefully at the roots, at the base of the clumps of grass, one could see a soft, sparse tinge of green, but no more.

Bristol had unhooked and removed his window for better vision and was heading for three giraffe, 'thinking aloud' quite informally as we drove along. He stopped when we reached them, took out his record book to compare neck markings, though he already knew exactly who we were looking at, and began to make notes. 'That's my oldest baby,' Bristol said, his eyes on the smallest giant. 'The mother is over there, and this one, with the "K" marking,' which I managed to see quite clearly, 'is a new companion.'

He explained how family groups seemed to change frequently, and that even the very young were often found far from their mothers. 'They seem to have little family feeling.' How strange and different from, for instance, the elephant or the gazelle, who fight tooth and nail to protect their young. Seventy-five per cent of young giraffe disappear completely before they are six months old. Mostly taken by predators, how many of those died because they were neglected by their mothers?

The three giraffe were feeding as we watched them, their irregular skin pattern blending harmoniously with the dull brown-grey of their surroundings. They were not feeding from high trees but from the almost ground-level 'whistling thorn', an incredibly sharp-needled bush which grew in profusion in that part of the Park. It is said that giraffe are about as 'thick on the ground' as, ecologically speaking, there is food for. Since they can adapt from tree-tops to a bush which they turn into bizarre hour-glass shapes looking like shear-trimmed hedge decorations, to low bush, even reeds and ground-level thickets, they should survive the danger of changing vegetation and encroaching humanity far better than some of the other species, which are dependent upon one type of food alone.

I asked Bristol whether the modern giraffe might, one day, evolve into a lower-legged, shorter-necked creature through low feeding, but he doubted it. Their height gave them the ability to see their predators, to adapt to temperatures, and perhaps had other advantages of which high feeding was only one. He would not let my imagination run away with me; he was, above all, a scientist, even if he did wear a dreamy, faraway look sometimes, mingled with a sort of ethereal, Peter Pannish touch. Years of behaviourist studies, where just 'looking' and accurate recording meant the difference between failure and success, had taught him to be cautious of surmise!

After the giraffe, he wanted to find a certain lark, he knew exactly which one. The subject matter for his observations was certainly contrasting, perhaps a factor for the survival of the biologist-behaviourist who often grows to look like the animal he is studying!

Leaving the eastern side of the Park, we met two young male cheetah on the prowl whom Bristol knew well. Apart from his own interest, he was supervising various students who were embarking on animal studies, and one of these was following the progress of the cheetah. They were lean, empty bellied, regal, with not an extra inch anywhere that would hinder their lightning progress once they gathered speed.

Bristol slowly followed the pair as they divided, circled and united in their search for food. The hartebeest, seeing them, retreated, then stopped and took some steps towards them, straining its head in their direction, as if needing a last-minute satisfaction that he really did have something to run away from. Gazelle were more cautious and just galloped off, a thousand times more graceful than the top-heavy sloping hartebeest. After some time the cheetah, quite unperturbed by the rain, went down a slope to the river and rocks and there we left them, a little disappointed not to see the outcome of their hunt, yet for my part, relieved, too. To see a kill was a divided joy, somehow almost too macabre to recall with any pleasure.

It was getting late and the rain had stopped. Bristol found the little bush on which the lark was vocally marking out his territory with its shrill whistle. He had filmed the bird and now wanted to record its voice. But we were too late, having been too long following the cheetah. While the lark's exquisite red throat quivered with song the sky vibrated with jet-plane droning and the murmur of small planes coming in to land at the nearby airport. Bristol, disappointed, unscrewed his reflecting gear. He was leaving Africa within two months and his chances to watch, photograph and record were getting fewer and fewer.

Both of us had to be back by ten o'clock. We took another route, passing groups of sleek-buttocked Burchell zebra, so fat that they seemed to bounce as they ran. A family of seven wart-hog, always late risers on a dull day, were busy feeding at the side of the road, an ox-pecker perched on the back of the male. We passed wildebeest, even darker looking with their skins wet, long-tailed and skittish in the cool morning. When we reached the main gate we stopped at the attractively built Director's Headquarters and Parks Offices which form the centre of operations of the Kenya Park's system.

Dennis Kearney, the Warden, and his wife were both there, already in the throes of their impending departure. I could not imagine the Park without them. Dennis, popular with visitors, as easy with special V.I.P.s as with anyone else, had a good knowledge of his park and its inhabitants. He had been in Nairobi for five years; during that time the Park had thrived and passed many hurdles. Directorship had changed hands, policies were changing, too, but Dennis had managed to steer clear of trouble, supported by his wife, Yuilleen, who acted as overflow for the wild animal orphanage of the Nairobi National Park, 'Animals are my life,' she told me. She had grown up on a farm at Naivasha and had raised many animals, from cheetah to rhino.

It was to treat her latest patient that she first called me. Though she knew far more than I did about the raising of rhinos, there were still some veterinary aspects with which I could help. Yuilleen had written a book, *Rufus the Rhino*, in which she told of the step-by-step experiences of bringing up the orphan. She was most successful, and Rufus had survived the difficult weaning years. When the Kearneys left Tsavo National Park, he had been adopted by Daphne Sheldrick, wife of the Warden, and finally, still attached to humans whom he obviously considered his own kind, allowed himself, in the company of two elephants and two buffalo, to be herded into suitable pasture by day, returning home to his own stable at night.

We called the new arrival 'Tinker Bell', for the simple reason that never in my life could I have visualized anything less fairy-like than the four-day-old black rhinoceros baby which I found waiting for me on the sun-warmed steps at the

Kearney house. Their home was some minutes' drive from the main gate, a journey I always enjoyed immensely, for often, and especially in the evening hours, various animals congregated near the roadside. Just beyond the place where I reluctantly left a beautiful herd of buffalo one night, one could see a sloping bank on the right where giraffe almost always had their heads down looking for salt. All too soon one arrived at the fork in the road, the left being marked 'private', unmistakable by the addition of the skull, white and enormous, of an elephant, the one we had used in one of our *Animal Ark* programmes.

Dennis and Yuilleen's home was set beautifully at the top of a hill, the new dam not far below; accessible, yet quite remote, part and parcel of the Park itself. Lions, leopard, cheetah, rhino and many others also felt that way about it and at times made free use of their very large garden, which, though fenced, merged naturally into the rest of the Sanctuary. I was met by the daughter of the house at my first visit: very small, golden-haired, with eyes deep blue and large as saucers. Maureen, by a series of hops and head turnings to make sure I was following her, led me to the front open stone veranda where I found her mother and the patient with umbilical cord still attached, absorbed in each other's presence. What a contrast they were! Yuilleen pretty, dark-haired, fine-skinned and slightly podgy. The rhino, about one foot above the ground, anything but lovely, thin as a rake, ribs protruding, skin rough, unhealthy, a mud-coloured brown. My first thought was, 'I can't believe it!' The rhino, a female, seemed incredibly ugly, but then so had my, now glamorous, niece seemed ugly for the first week after birth!

They got up, introductions unnecessary, and I went over to my patient at once to examine her. She was taking her bottle, but not too willingly, Yuilleen said, and we looked inside her mouth where the cause so often lay. Yuilleen had suspected ulcers and she was absolutely right. They were in the throat and on the gums, raw, infected, as great an obstacle to healthy growth, and indeed in an animal, to survival, as they would be in a new-born baby. 'Stinkie', as the rhino came to be called for reasons obvious to her keepers (although it was, at the same time, also a natural abbreviation of Tinker Bell) had to have her mouth sprayed and for the first time she balked. Yuilleen stood behind and astride to stop her slipping away while I, holding her mouth open, placed the aerosol spray in such a position as to direct the contents in the proper direction. I warned Yuilleen that it might misfire, remembering Toni's classic story of a similar situation.

He had, many years ago, been confronted by a lady whose dachshund needed external application for a skin condition. In those days jet-sprays were new, their mechanics largely unexplored by many practitioners. The dog was most intractible and had to be held. Toni suggested that the best way to restrain it would be to stretch it across the lady's bosom. The client, probably too amazed and embarrassed to object, did as she was asked. Toni pressed the button and released a flow of purple spray which did not at all restrict itself to the direction he had intended. Instead of one stream, a large violet cloud emanated, with the result that everything in front of him received equal treatment. When the lady, who no doubt had some inkling of the disaster, took down the dog, she was entirely purple, leaving a clearly defined dachshund shape upon her breast, topped by the circles of her startled eyes. For some reason Toni could not comprehend why she curtly refused his kind offer to fill in the blank space!

I was a little more successful than he had been, knowing, after years of aerosol medication, what to expect. Just as I was opening the rhino jaws for the third and last time, I heard a most unusual sound, a sort of muted, plaintive cry, neither human nor animal. I stopped, diverted from my purpose and found Yuilleen smiling up at me in that very mischievous, girlish way of hers. 'That's rhino talk,' she said. 'They make that sound all through their life, although it becomes more loud and intense as they grow older. Apart from snorting as they charge through the bush, this is the sum-total of their vocabulary—with variations, of course, which we cannot understand.' It was hard to believe. This, one of the fiercest creatures of Africa, with such a soft and ineffectual voice!

I thought back upon the young giraffe which Toni had darted in the Kruger National Park and which demonstrated its vocal chords (which so many doubt it possesses) with the most ovine, undignified bleat. How had all this evolved? The elephant, family conscious, was very talkative, very demonstrative, and his trumpeting, screaming and rumbling seemed to suit his character well. Giraffe, I had learnt from Bristol Foster, were not very social creatures, nor did they protect their young as did the elephant. Therefore vocalization was not, perhaps, necessary; they seemed satisfied in sparring with their necks, weaving and banging them upon each other in play and in attack. The hook-lipped, 'black' rhinoceros, such as Stinkie was, was a solitary animal, mostly keeping to himself rather than living in a group. So he had little need to communicate, yet his snorts and grunts as he charged, were as terrifying as the lowered, powerful head and pointed horn.

What an enormous field of research for those who were tempted to translate the sounds of the wild! Perhaps man would not really know until he was able to lift himself above himself on to a higher level of understanding. Perhaps communication with the wild could not be attempted until he had put his own house in order, for peace of mind or lack of it must have some effect on the sensitive animal receptor system. It was all a matter of tuning in, first to one's self and thereby to the higher worlds; somewhere along the way we could achieve an understanding quite beyond that of our earthly plane and this, in turn, would lead us to greater perception of the kingdom of the animals.

Helped by Dennis and Maureen, Yuilleen created a real home atmosphere for the rhino. At first I hardly believed that it would survive. After a month or two, during which we had to treat it for an infected hernia and digestive upsets, it picked up in condition, drank its four-hourly bottle avidly, and began to lose that heavy-headed, three-feet-in-the-grave look which I had seen on the day of our first meeting. Its rapid improvement was not only due to good milk and food and veterinary treatment. It was, to a large extent, due to the fact that it had a mother's—though she was human—attention each hour of the day, and not one minute less. 'A baby animal can sense whether you really love it,' Yuilleen told me. 'When it knows that, then it grows confident. It *knows* because it can scent your love.' She was sure that one did not only give out a 'fear' scent, but also one denoting affection, and that without it, rearing a young animal was very difficult. When she took an orphan or sick animal into her care, then they came first; the family had to understand and to adjust. Yet in such a family hardly any adjustments had to be made, for they knew and understood that this was the only way for rearing the really young, of any species.

From Yuilleen and Dennis—and Maureen—I learnt a great deal about devotion and single-mindedness. I visited them about once a week during that period of Stinkie's early life. The body bandage, which my patient kept on quite dutifully, helped to control the hernia after the initial infection had healed. The bouts of diarrhoea and constipation were not insurmountable either. After four months, at which time the rhino had doubled its height and weighed about 150 pounds of solid muscle, Yuilleen decided that she must tear herself away from the constant minute-by-minute care which Stinkie no longer needed for her survival. Bottle feeding had to continue for a very long time, for in the wild the mother continues to feed the young for four years. Malutu, their animal-man, a young African who had a way with animals, was appointed to keep the rhino company during the day, for she still needed companionship for continued happiness. The dogs and cat kept her some company but not constantly; they were simply all lodgers in the same household. Maureen often played with Stinkie with abandonment to their mutual enjoyment. To see them together, rolling on the ground, chasing each other on the lawns, riding astride the rhino's back was a marvellous sight. They had become close friends. As the rhino grew, Maureen grew, too, but in the end Stinkie became too rough a playmate. I thought that the Kearneys might pass her on to the orphanage for peace and quiet and an interlude until the next patient arrived. But I was wrong. By the time the next patient came the house had settled into a rhino routine, the sleeping place had been changed from the bedroom to lounge, then to infra-red heated sleeping quarters outside. Malutu by day, with Kearneys in between to keep the link and prepare the milk formula and other food as it advanced in its tastes and needs. It was all settled and beautifully regular, until the advent of Helen, the orphan elephant. When she arrived, the turmoil, the sleepless nights, the daily disruption began all over again, restoring this animal household to its normal sequence of organized disorder.

13 *Crossed Tusks and Mother Love*

I WAS RELIEVED it was elephants. Playing second fiddle to any other creature, human or animal, would almost certainly have wrecked our new marriage at once. I did think it rather strange to begin with. After all, we were starry-eyed newly-weds who had known each other for eighteen years; when a man marries a girl at the sober age of forty he *should* know what his priorities are. But Toni could not see my view at all; he felt that I should have been aware of his inmost feelings, and that I would never have loved him had he been any different. First came his philosophy (which was as it should be), and then the elephants; then a long gap, followed by me in the rear.

It took Helen, the little orphan, to teach me about the wonder of the elephant. I came to know her rather intimately over a period of nearly two months, which gave me a better understanding of her kind. I had to admit in the end that, young though she was, she possessed a quality bordering on the mystical; not just intelligence or an attractive personality but something very different from any animal I had ever met. After that, I, too, joined the ranks of the elephant fans and looked upon them with the veneration which is their due.

She was brought in by a professional hunter who had been camping near a dried-up watering place near Kajiado, a township on the way south between Kenya and Tanzania. All through the night there had been a tremendous elephant com- motion; although the party did not dare approach too closely they did manage to find the cause of the uproar. A small elephant had somehow become trapped in a hole and the herd was making frantic attempts to lift it out. They could hear the baby crying pitifully, but by the time dawn came the herd had left and all sound abated. Certain that the elephant baby must have died, the hunter nevertheless went out to investigate and found, to his amazement, that the creature was still very much alive. Buried in a mud-hole to her head she had exhausted herself by her efforts to scramble out and by the time he reached her she had resigned herself to her ghastly fate.

It must have taken quite an effort to extricate the mud-covered, slippery orphan. When she arrived at the wild animal orphanage, she was not only very dehydrated and her feet terribly chafed and cracked from her night-long efforts at scrambling out of the hole, but also very shocked and bewildered at having lost her mother. I went to see her two days after she arrived. She was thought to be six weeks old and stood just under two feet six inches at the shoulder, weighing nearly four hundred pounds. Though in a completely strange environment, she had already accepted human and animal companions. I thought that her chance of survival in the very busy, rather over-populated animal orphanage was less than if she could receive more individual attention with a great deal of foster-mother love thrown in.

I smiled the question at Yuilleen, hardly daring to suggest that she take on yet another burden when she had barely recovered from her vigil of Stinkie. 'Yes, I know what you want me to do,' she had caught my meaning at once. 'I'll walk her down to the house and keep her there. She and the rhino will be good playmates.'

How she knew they would be I really could not guess, for in my ignorance I would have thought that two more opposing animal characters hardly existed. I had recently seen an aggressive, obstinate black rhinoceros charge a full-grown elephant. They had been competing for a salt lick at a dam; the rhino had arrived second on the scene but did not have the good grace to wait its turn. With an immense show of

Everyone would take a rest after the game—Maureen, Helen,
Stinkie and the tricycle

The author examines the rhino's mouth

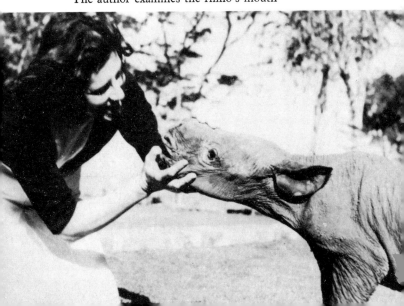

Howard Baldwin suturing a radio transmitter onto an elephant's neck, with a helping hand from the author

valour and amidst much grunting and snorting it charged, horn down, towards the elephant bull. The latter lifted his trunk as if to scent the intruder, brought forward his ears a little, as if to hear him better, but unlike the grandmother-wolf in Red Riding Hood, did not take one step forward in aggression. As if endowed with a superior intelligence and a dislike for argument, he backed away with dignity, then turned and left.

Would Helen and Stinkie see eye to eye? Would they not vie for love from their foster-mother and end up fighting, even one-sidedly, in the process? Yuilleen, as always, had been right. The two orphans, as different to look at as chalk and cheese, almost fell into each other's arms, if one can use such an expression in describing two animals. Their needs, their baby-habits and sense of play came to the fore as if they were part of a team. Stinkie was off the danger list and needed less attention by the time Helen came. She was larger than the rhino by virtue of her heritage and more powerful in spite of her foot injuries and dehydration. Yuilleen decided to give the elephant a full-time companion as well as a playmate and found a young billy-goat who joined in the fun and slept with her at night. Helen refused, like an obstinate child, to go to her grass-padded hut without the goat; when it was time for sleep they bedded down side by side, the elephant's infantile trunk curled round her sleeping partner.

I paid frequent visits to the Park. The feet needed to be dressed and checked, and eventually four beautiful boots were made and put on the very tender feet. The digestive system caused trouble but responded well to systematic medication. Not very long after my first meeting I grew to love that little elephant as I had never loved an animal before, in spite of the fact that it was not my own. She used to rumble whenever she was touched between her front legs, her response to the comfort gesture which the mother elephant gives her baby several times a minute. The goat, the rhino, Yuilleen and her daughter Maureen, who loved them all, took the place of one mother elephant and under their care she thrived. African baby elephants are the most difficult of all to rear; rarely has anyone succeeded when the orphan is so small and needs four-hourly bottle feeding. It seems that elephant milk is high in fats which are of a special nature, something so unique that a substitute has not yet been found. We all produced ideas, different formulas from different sources. The one that Yuilleen used seemed to succeed and the elephant grew. She had minor troubles such as eye and mouth infections, but no more than a growing baby of any other species.

I had never had a patient like her before. Although she was attached to Yuilleen more than to anyone else, she allowed herself to be approached, provided she approved. Lifting her trunk in that typical elephantine gesture of 'scent to size up', she took a very good look as well, and, if she did find the stranger to her liking, she would then approach and touch him. When she began to rumble it was like a compliment which I felt proud to receive. I liked nothing better than to sit on the grass and watch her at play with her animal chums and Maureen, the four of them tumbling about the slope at the edge of the garden like a football team. They would race up and down chasing one, then turn about and chase the other. The goat loved it, too, but sometimes found the game a little rough; after all, what is a few pounds of goat compared with the solid mass of rhino or elephant, infant though they be! In the end, after a series of bouts, everyone would take a rest on the soft sandy earth or in the grass, Maureen's tricycle included.

After six weeks, Helen became very ill. She had seemed quieter and slower on the day we made our elephant programme for *Animal Ark*. She had been most co-operative and affectionate, allowed herself to be fed 'in camera' and posed beautifully so that her small size could be compared to that of the huge adult elephant skull.

Nevertheless, both Yuilleen and Dennis, who loved the orphans as much as the rest of the family, felt that something was wrong with the elephant baby, especially when she didn't want to play on the next day. She was showing signs of digestive trouble and of course our first thought was the formula. We changed it slightly by diluting the milk content and adding a mixture of medicaments which had always succeeded in curing any rhino imbalance.

But Helen showed no signs of improvement. Instead, her condition worsened and she developed a complicating lung and heart infection. She received antibiotic therapy but even that did not help. After three days she became too weak to move about the garden and remained in her own house, taking little food. On the last day of her life I decided that she was in pain and gave her additional sedation, for, above all, I did not want her to suffer from either discomfort or fear. I closed myself up with her for several hours, the only way really to assess her state. She responded to me, quite aware of my presence, but could not make the effort to do more than give a weak sign of recognition. Her breathing was laboured, her heartbeat fast and stressed. Someone suggested that I should destroy her to put her out of her misery, but again, and with Yuilleen's approval, I decided against it. I had seen so many last moment recoveries, so many miraculous cures; as long as I was certain that the elephant wasn't suffering unduly there was no more to be done.

Suddenly, about mid-morning, Helen's breathing slowed down and steadied, she sat up, turned towards me and lifted her head so that her eyes were level with mine. It cost her quite an effort to do this but she seemed quite determined. I noticed something different about her eyes, for they contained a look which seemed to penetrate beyond the realm of our earthly existence. She stayed like that for nearly a minute during which time I remembered that I had seen that kind of ethereal gaze before in the eyes of a clairvoyant lady who saw beyond into other worlds, past, present and future. Then, as the thought passed, Helen gave a soft, long groan which ended in a whispering sigh, more human than animal. If any sound could ever mean the release of a tired soul, then it was that last breath of the little elephant. I stayed with her until the heart had stopped completely, until any vestige of physical movement had disappeared. Even then I could hardly bring myself to return to the business of living, of transmitting the news to those who had expected it for days. On post-mortem, it was found that Helen had died of heart lesions, and not of the usual cause of infant elephant death: stomach and intestinal ulceration caused by an unsuitable feeding formula.

I felt an acute ache of grief and loss such as one usually feels when one has lost someone very dear whom one has known for a lifetime. It had only been six weeks, but then, who can tell whether Helen had been with us before or not? That last look she had given me haunted me for days and months; when the sadness of parting had lessened and I could think back without feeling that terrible tug at my heart-strings, I began to realize the inherent nobility and depth of character of the apparently helpless orphan much more clearly.

I began to watch elephants with more concentration and attention whenever we visited a National Park or Game Reserve, or saw them along the road outside sanctuaries. I had been teaching my *Animal Ark* children about how to make observations, yet I had myself never *really looked* at the largest mammal on land: a huge body, trunk and spreading ears, the tail which ended in a switch of much-coveted elephant hair. I had usually noted the length of the tusks, the weight of the body, the flat round feet. Now I was beginning to notice many other things, like the silent light-footedness, the sudden un-heralded appearance and equally mysterious merging with the trees and even the shadows of the trees. I began to look *into* the face and *at* the eyes, but always we were either too far away or time was short. Somewhere, surely there must be a man, or even a woman, who was studying the behaviour of the African elephant, just as many others were studying the behaviour of other creatures. More difficult, without doubt, perhaps more dangerous; yet this was the era of the elephant and unless the biologists pulled up their socks and conducted scientific long-term studies, the elephant was in danger of being cropped and disturbed out of existence. To have to take life when many elephants were already being killed by hunters was inexcusable—yet it was being done—and, at last, being noticed! Since we are the guardians of the wild, since they have been entrusted into our care, it is up to us to find a way of learning about them without too much interference to their natural behaviour or environment.

The first time I heard of the existence of an elephant behaviourist was when the conference of Land Use was being held in Nairobi. Our friend, Ian McTaggart Cowan, the world-renowned zoologist, had come all the way from Vancouver to present a paper and had begun his stay in East Africa by visiting Parks and scientist camps. Bristol Foster, who had been one of Ian's students, had taken him to Lake Manyara National Park for the main purpose of introducing him to Iain Douglas-Hamilton, who was studying elephant behaviour. 'Never been so frightened in my life,' was his dry comment of the experience. 'That young man took us right under the trunks of the elephants.'

I could imagine what a sobering experience it must have been, especially when Iain was plunged headlong into elephants without any previous conditioning. Still, how else could one really get a good look at the trunk of an elephant except by getting very close? 'I wish he would invite us to visit him,' I thought with longing. 'Perhaps Toni will be asked to work there.' It should be heaven for a man who prefers elephants to his wife, and since wives' tastes are supposed to follow their men's, it might also be heaven for me.

Not too long after, an American radio-telemetric expert—that rare breed of men who not only know how to use this intensely complicated equipment, but also how to make it—arrived in Nairobi to see us. Howard Baldwin had been working in the Serengeti with other biologists; he had brought radio-telemetric apparatus with him and had used it on lion and hyena. The former had tolerated their signal-sending collars quite well, the latter, in true hyena fashion, had somehow either managed to rid themselves of their artificial appendages in record time or damaged them beyond recognition. Howard's interest was linked with Toni's research work in many ways. They were both engaged in recording physio-

197

logical functions by means of the radio-senders placed in or on the animal. Howard was more absorbed in the technical side, while Toni, as a physiologist with an immense interest in the normal function of the large wild African animal, was using similar equipment for the discovery of basic animal reactions and adjustment to their environment. Iain Douglas-Hamilton, as an elephant-behaviourist, was interested in the movement of his elephant herds and their social interplay. Since they moved fast and far, this was difficult. If one of his herd could wear a collar and emit signals which could be picked up by a directional aerial, then he could locate them day or night, thus making his study a biologist's dream.

Both Howard and Iain needed Toni's help. They needed him for the primary immobilization, for the veterinary aspects of the work and for a co-ordinate effort of radio-telemetry on an animal that had never been radio-telemetrized before. After a great deal of discussion and writing of letters the post-Christmas period was decided on. The children would be away at that time and we could cut our intended two weeks at the coast to one. We were both tired and needed a holiday. This kind of safari, which would take us into one of the loveliest Parks in Tanzania and at the same time would mean a worthwhile piece of research work, appealed to us enormously.

Perhaps if it had not been quite so cloudy at the Kialifi coast on the day of our departure we might have regretted leaving that glorious sea and our lotus-eating days of absolute tranquillity. As it was, we left quite cheerfully, the feeling of Nairobi rush washed well out of our veins, the look of tired gauntness gone from Toni's face. We drove first to Voi to see the Warden and his wife, David and Daphne Sheldrick, who had kindly kept Toni's capture gun for us while we were at the coast. Daphne had just returned from Paris after her lightning visit to receive a prize for her beautiful book of animal experiences, *The Orphans of Tsavo*. The glamour of Paris in the snow, of being wined and dined, of flashing camera bulbs wherever she went, had worn her out completely. She was terribly glad to be home, and we would have loved to have stayed a little longer to listen to her adventures, but, as always, time was short and we were expected at Manyara that evening.

We finally arrived at 9 p.m., so late that Iain had returned to his own camp which was about half an hour's drive deep into the Park. A room had been prepared for us at the guesthouse and we were most grateful for it. An assistant warden made us welcome and showed us the ropes, which included a self-sufficient kitchen-dining-room with running water and gas. It was too late for dinner and we were far too tired to eat. I found a tin of soup at the bottom of our supply box and that was enough. We collapsed into bed to the accompaniment of the sound of flowing water near by, one of the most soothing, soporific sounds in the world.

I think I shall always associate the sound of water flowing on rock with elephants, for a magnificent waterfall above provided the theme song of Iain's forest home. 'It reminds me of Scotland,' he said, showing us around when we arrived, 'perhaps that is why I chose the site.' I would wager a guess that his base of operations is situated more beautifully than any other in Africa; perhaps he deserves his luck for having chosen the most splendid of all creatures as the object of his study. On the morning after arrival we had eaten our second breakfast with him and admired his wooden and stone living-study-bedroom which he had himself designed and which was built by local artisans. The camp spread upwards from there; first a little guest hut which was to be ours, then another at the top nearest the waterfall, which was Iain's. From there one looked down upon a rock-pool frequented by herds of different animals in the drier season when water is a centralizing point.

We had just met each other and the Baldwin husband and wife team, so we decided to spend at least some hours—which eventually turned into a day—working out a plan, checking on equipment and assessing the location. Iain, a bespectacled, handsome shaggy-haired Oxford graduate, was unusually systematic and tidy—even neat—and had already spent two years at Manyara, the first half of his elephant study period. He had longed for Africa from the time when, at the age of seven, he had read the South African story, *Jock of the Bushveld*. Being a determined young man, he had stuck to his guns and had eventually, after graduating as a zoologist, fulfilled his dream of working among the wild.

Having taken us on our first reconnaisance drive after which I perfectly understood Iain Cowan's sentiments, I asked him whether he had always been so courageous in his approach of elephant. 'Not on your life,' he smiled, his boyish, almost mischievous smile, 'when I began to work here I disappeared every time an elephant shook his head.' It had taken him about three months before he had called the first elephant's bluff. He had spent the time just watching the herds, getting to know the individual members, devising a way of recognition which excluded marking. 'They're all quite different,' he assured us, just as we approached a group of cows and calves. 'Let me show you.' He then proceeded to acquaint us with the herd leader, 'Boadicea,' who was accompanied by seven others of different size, from very large to very small. Boadicea lifted her trunk and made as if to charge as we came to a sudden halt, her huge ears spreading as she trumpeted. 'Take no notice of her,

she's just bad-tempered,' he assured us, 'but do look at that tiny toto (baby).' Perhaps he was trying to distract us and if he was, then it was excellent psychology, for the elephant baby was so small and so new that my attention was completely diverted from any other thought. As we watched, she began to suck, her trunk somehow tucked out of the way, her mouth only just reaching the distended breasts behind the front legs. Boadicea had meanwhile stopped her demonstration but was still keeping a very wary eye on us all. When Iain started up the Land-Rover I found that I really hadn't been frightened at all, and looking at Toni I saw that he, too, seemed as calm as ever. Well, Iain should know what he was doing and the fact that he claimed to know each elephant's disposition helped a great deal.

'Have you ever been wrong?' I asked him, and the next moment I was sorry that I had broached the subject, for I would much rather have kept my faith and illusions than lose them.

'Just once an elephant charged and went on,' he told us. 'I had parked and was just waiting for a herd to appear when a huge unfamiliar cow elephant, probably from the hunting area in the south, broke through the undergrowth towards me, hitting me with terrific impact. Perhaps she could not stop but wanted to,' he tried to reassure us. 'She probably didn't know I was there, and when she saw me just lost her head. Unfortunately others followed suit and in the end the Land-Rover side was gored and we were dragged over thirty-five yards.'

'We,' I said, horrified, 'who was with you?'

'A girl who was visiting me,' he explained, 'and she never came back,' he added wistfully. 'She got into a heap on the floor while I just hunched myself into the smallest possible shape and waited.' He demonstrated, curling himself up over the steering wheel and showed us how the tusks had pierced the Land-Rover side with no window over it, and just missed him narrowly. 'I want reinforced doors,' he said, 'then I'd feel safer.'

Lake Manyara National Park is very small; no larger than

Nairobi Park. Thirty-five square miles of dry land, and another eighty-eight of lake. The vegetation ranges from lush ground-water forest, which forms the northern sector as one enters the gate, to grassland and marshy lakeside and thick hilly woodland, where the greatest trees of Africa grow in profusion; the yellow-barked fever tree and the inverted baobab, huge spreading figs and palms; the tamarind and 'sausage tree,' and the most characteristic of all, the *Acacia tortilis*, the 'umbrella tree,' with its spreading irregular roof of twisted, gnarled branches. The Manyara lions, renowned for their tree-climbing habits, love these trees more than any other and we often found them lazily sprawled along the branches, their limply hanging tails and legs sometimes the only hint of their presence. Iain took us up to one of these trees on the first day; we counted seven satiated, half-awake lions, their lair an excellent vantage point over that whole area. Did they just drop down on their unsuspecting prey without having to stalk? Apparently not, for we were told by Jonathan Mahanga, the enthusiastic warden of the Park, that apart from their affection for trees, they hunted as other lions in other places. Since the park is neatly contained between escarpment and lake, few of the animals move far away. Three hundred elephants, giraffe, wildcats and predators, buffalo, many species of antelope, zebra and black rhinoceros as well as a wealth of birdlife, about three hundred species, notably flocks of flamingos and pelicans, make this a wildlife showplace.

We were getting our bearings. It always took me a great deal longer than Toni, for I seemed to have been born with one group of brain cells missing—the group which is responsible for one's sense of direction. As I hardly ever had to drive alone, and then usually only on the main paths, I managed to avoid making a nuisance of myself by getting lost. Manyara would be a difficult place to get lost in, even for me, with the escarpment on one side and the lake on the other. The only confusion could arise in the thick forest which Iain had chosen for operations on the first day. We were all prepared and ready to go, having decided to work from two vehicles, one short-wheel-base Land-Rover which was much more manoeuvrable, but could normally only seat two, and the Baldwins' Land-Rover, long-base with plenty of room which would house us: Howard, Dorothy and me and the rest of the equipment. We had a set of walkie-talkie radios which were absolutely essential for the project. We had to keep in touch and discovered, very soon, that the communications system was to be our life-line.

I believe that everyone, including the warden and the scouts, thought that the first day of our operations would bring success. How could it be otherwise? Toni had years of immobilizing experience behind him which included elephant, and Howard was an expert at making alterations on just about anything under makeshift conditions. Iain knew his elephants and would guide us towards bulls, which were safe and suitable to dart. The radio-telemetric part of it, including the big, adjustable collar which contained the directional sender, should not cause any difficulty either. As a team we seemed well suited, a most important factor, since under the stresses and strains of this kind of work, any incompatibilities could become very accentuated. The Director of Parks, John Owen, had given his blessing and Hugh Lamprey, the Director of the Research Institute of which Iain was part, had been very enthusiastic. Had we known then how heaven was about to try us we might not have felt quite so confident that morning three days after Christmas.

The elephant herds, which usually moved down from the escarpment into the bush and forest and then to the lake, could not be found. Iain was terribly distressed, even angry, for how could 300 elephants possibly disappear in the course of one night.

We tried to console him while we drank cup after cup of coffee. 'They knew we were coming,' Toni said, 'it often happens like this. We're sending out the wrong vibrations.' But in the early afternoon part of the herd reappeared and Iain selected a young male named 'Chisel-tusks,' estimated to weigh about 9000 pounds, as the first victim. Another young male, apparently sensing that his herdmate was in need of help, tagged along, both heading for rather thicker vegetation than would allow a vehicle to pass'

'We have put a dart into an elephant,' came the message through the radio. 'Left high rump.' That meant also that we should stay where we were until further instructions. Our backs to the lake, dotted with flamingos and pelicans, we faced the hills, a black stormcloud perched on the edge as if about to roll over any moment like an avalanche. As we waited, a second herd of fourteen appeared out of the thick undergrowth and passed behind towards the lake, and as they did we heard a loud trumpeting from the direction Iain and Toni had taken. My heart missed a beat, but I collected myself as the radio aerial, up and ready, crackled for attention. 'Elephant swaying, drug taking effect.' That was twenty-seven minutes after darting, not bad at all, I reflected hopefully. 'He's only fifty yards away now,' came Iain's whispered message. 'Don't reply. I repeat, don't reply.'

'Like something out of a mystery story sequence,' I said to Dorothy as we waited with bated breath.

It had not occurred to us that Iain and Toni were now on foot, a very hazardous way of following elephant when one could hardly see more than a few yards ahead. They carried a large-calibre gun, it was true, but who would have time to use it if a rhino, as once happened to Iain, charged out at them from behind a clump of bush! 'Not really ideal elephant-darting country,' Toni said as he reached the Land-Rover. He had left Iain behind, on his own insistence, and was driving round to the other end of the thicket to try to locate the elephant.

A few moments after he had gone Iain appeared, gun slung over his shoulder, for the two elephants were still on the move away from the hills. 'Better follow them in case we lose sight,' he said, climbing into his own vehicle which Toni had brought back, and as he got in I jumped into the open back, no longer able to contain my impatience at having to wait without knowing what was happening either to them or the elephant. 'Okay with me,' Iain said when I asked him if he minded, and strangely enough Toni made no objection either, his attention probably on other matters.

We drove towards the lake a little way and across the grassland, making a wide circle as we did so. I had spotted another herd moving towards us, eleven strong, one enormous cow leading the group; Iain stopped and waited for them. To him, apart from the value of our project, this was just another chance for his observations and for further marking their positions on his chart. He turned on his tape-recorder and softly spoke into it, a simple report which would be broken down later. I was almost mesmerized by the sight of the cross-tusked giant now slowing down as she saw that we were not giving way. As she did so she trumpeted shrilly, her enormous ears moving back and forth, the young mothers and infants gathered closely behind her, as if enveloped in a protective cloak.

'Take no notice, it's just Sarah being neurotic again.' Iain soothed, as the huge cow sounded her defiance. I felt very naked and vulnerable in the open truck, and bent down in an effort to make myself invisible. 'Isn't she beautiful, look at her crossed tusks and her long ears,' Iain soliloquized. 'She is a bit aggressive, but I think she'll go on.' Again, I forgot to feel frightened, though my ducking movement certainly didn't reveal great bravery. I could not help but admire her fiercely protective mother love, even as she made a rush at our vehicle. She must have been in the swamps not long before, for her legs were muddy and wet up to the knees. With an angry toss of her head and trunk, and trumpeting a scream of final farewell, she moved on and away, her dependants behind her. 'Okay?' asked Iain as he started up the engine. 'You won't forget her in a hurry!'

The darted elephant, dart still attached to the rump, was recovering. The dose had not been sufficient and in a few hours he would be quite normal. It was our first disappointment and that night we discussed all the pros and cons of heavier dosing. Toni was all against it, for to him the life of the elephant was far more important than quick, but danger-fraught success. Iain felt the same way, but even more strongly. At the end of the exercise, whenever that was to be, he wanted 300 elephants alive and not one less!

'It's nothing more or less than the normal difficulties of a new field operation,' Toni insisted. True, everything that could go wrong did go wrong; elusive elephants, faulty equipment, unpredictable drug response. A damaged sump, a few flat tyres and many narrow escapes—yet, what was all that when weighed against freedom from accident and ultimate success? The darts were our first headache. Some bounced out and back, others broke, some needles did not discharge the full complement of drug. Reinforcements had to be brought in from the Serengeti Research Institute half a day's drive away, and more precious time was lost.

One mid-afternoon, the three men had gone on to select a young male, leaving us to wait in a particularly lovely glade not far from the lake. Dorothy Baldwin, in her enthusiasm and with eternal optimism and devotion to duty (she was an invaluable assistant to her husband) had once again raised the aerial and prepared the receiving equipment. If an elephant were successfully darted, he might go down within ten to twenty minutes and then everything would be needed at the same time. I would have to be ready for action with instruments to assist Howard, with blood bottles to take elephant blood samples for research purposes, take the temperature, clean the incision site where the thermister was to be buried for superficial recording and generally assist anyone else who needed assistance. Dorothy was quite right: one had to be at the ever-ready!

Thus, all prepared, we sat peacefully in our glade, listening to the hornbills braying, the tauracos giving the alarm— perhaps to the elephants?—writing our notes, talking of many things, but nothing in particular. When the forest on the lake-side began to rustle and crackle we thought nothing of it, for not even the approaching herd of elephants, led by the cow we now recognized as Portia, could disturb our equanimity. They slowly approached, feeding all the way, scented us, approached right up to the Land-Rover, and went on. Their mood was the same as ours: nothing—or so we thought—could have induced them at that moment to break the quietude of the afternoon. A rhino suddenly appeared, snorting and sniffing and entering the glade amidst the elephants, looking neither to left nor right. Remembering the previous elephant-rhino episode on the Aberdares, I waited for action; but none came, even the rhino had caught the feeling of 'live and let live' that pervaded our gap in the forest.

Then Dorothy, her ears more alert than mine, thought she heard a sharp report, which was neither an elephant gun nor the puff from the carbon dioxide discharge of the dart-gun. The radio-telephone was up, the right channel on the air, now all we could do was to sit tight and wait for news. Portia's herd had disappeared completely and we were, once more, alone, now tensed, sitting on the bonnet with binoculars, trying to find some clue which would give us the direction from which the shot had come. The radio signal sounded its code and we turned it on. 'We can hear you, please transmit; over.'

Iain's voice was urgent. 'We have a flat tyre and need your spare. We have darted an elephant, come quickly.' What Iain had forgotten to tell us was where he was, which he assumed we knew. First try took us in the wrong direction and again the radio sounded. 'Face the lake and keep driving,' Iain commanded tersely. They told us afterwards, in the comfort of the dining hut, that they had kept us in view, even as we drove in various directions trying to locate them. We gathered, and could well imagine, that some of the remarks passed as they watched us floundering round the bush had been far from complimentary!

By the time we reached them a few minutes later, the trumpeting and aggressive behaviour of the elephants had reached a peak. Portia and her herd had joined Boadicea and her group, all standing close to the newly darted elephant, a 5,000-pounder known as 'Sarah's Male.' They had formed a united firm front and looked ready to attack, frustrated that their threats and show of strength had made no impression on the stranded Land-Rover. Portia, gentle and peaceful only

207

half an hour back, looked the most warlike, her trumpeting echoing from hill to lake. Never, in the history of mankind, has a Land-Rover wheel been changed so quickly. For once Iain was as relieved as we were to leave, for a disabled vehicle and a herd of enraged elephant are two things that just don't go together. Luckily the dart had not been fully effective, for if it had the day might have ended quite differently. Not until the next afternoon, the most memorable of all those spent in Manyara, did we realize what a lucky escape we had had.

Had our group not been so utterly compatible, our seven-day adventure would never have reached success. The Baldwin pair, married only for as long as we had been, showed some signs of strain on the first day. Dorothy was impatient to get going, Howard to test his equipment. They were due to fly back to Arizona within two weeks and wanted, above all, to 'put that collar on an elephant.' No one had ever achieved this before and Howard yearned to be the first. The competitive 'bug' was as much part and parcel of his temperament as it was of any ambitious, highly efficient, progressive American. The slow English pace, the attitude that tomorrow is as good as today, was not his. Success was so near and yet so far; he relied on Toni to do his bit so that he could do his. The obstacles were growing, the days were passing and an immobile elephant was as far away as ever.

I think that, during the period of our first attempts, Desmond Morris saved the day. *The Naked Ape* was a book that Howard badly wanted to read but that had not yet reached East Africa. When he found it in Iain's library, sent by one of his female fans, he fell upon it and read it from cover to cover. While we waited in the Land-Rover we read it together, aloud to each other and when we reached the chapter on sex, quietly to ourselves!

We laughed, we discussed, we argued. Was Desmond Morris sincere in his best-seller views, was he really an atheist who rated mankind on monkey-level? There were so many hours of anxious waiting, when Toni and Iain, with or without Howard, entered the forest, when the screams and trumpets

Sarah, the cross-tusked cow elephant with her herd close behind

Girl, the lioness, fulfilling her duties as a mother

An immobilized zebra, for a wildlife sanctuary

Toni Harthoorn and Bill Winter, Game Warden of Nanyuki, who was an essential member of the rhino expedition

A telemetrized eland among its herd, quite unperturbed by the apparatus on its back. (Below) an eland which had been telemetrized with Toni Harthoorn holding the receiving set

Syringe in hand, I approached the giraffe

resounded like a nightmare, when we wondered if we would ever see any of them again, whole, alive and uninjured. The longer we had to wait, the more patient and easy-going the Baldwins became. It was as if they realized that good company and a sharp metaphorical rap on the knuckles to teach us the meaning of patience had come for a purpose, and provided a challenge.

Iain also had his moments of discontent, but he was only discontented with himself. He felt responsible for us all and the achievement of the project depended very largely on him too. He had to find and select the elephant to judge if it could be safely darted and whether the herd was distant enough to allow us to approach once the elephant went down. When a darted elephant was lost he blamed himself entirely but was optimistic that in the end we would win. Young though he was, he had, at twenty-five, learnt the art of waiting and knew how to be humble. At night he played us beautiful music on his portable record player, showed us the results of his work, and discussed elephant behaviour. All over his camp he had planted tree seeds that he had extricated from elephant dung, and they had grown quite high; he wanted to find out to what extent the elephant himself acted as reseeder of his own forests, as restorer of the habitat he sometimes destroyed.

Toni's patience was also being severely tried but whatever went on inside him did not show on the surface. He calmly continued from day to day, acting as a stress-reducing factor to the others and decided to use the time growing a beard. 'I'm practising extreme hirsutism,' he used to say, another of those words he relished and which no one else could understand. On checking up in the *Oxford Dictionary* to see if it really existed, I discovered the true meaning of 'hirsute' to be, 'hairy, shaggy, untrimmed'—an excellent description of his appearance at the time!

He would not allow himself to be hurried or pressurized into higher level dosing without gradually increasing the dose as he saw fit. As with Iain, the life of each elephant was important and if the work did take a little longer, what, after all, did it matter? No major step in research or wildlife work had ever been taken in only one week. Though the ground work of M99 had been done, no one had ever investigated species variation or tolerance to drugs between one locality of elephants and another. Though Toni outwardly showed little sign of strain, except our common tiredness at the end of the day, he lost every ounce I had rejoiced to see him gain during our week at the coast. Yet he was immensely happy to be in Manyara, for this was the work he loved more than anything else. Research on wild animals, another step forward towards conservation.

My own feelings varied from day to day and hour to hour. I was thrilled to be part of an elephant project, to be able to learn more about them, to work with someone whose sole object was to delve into their world. The environment of our work was ideal, our little group harmonious and friendly. Yet in those moments when we sat waiting for the radio to begin its beeps, when we heard the screams and crashes echo through the forest as Toni and Iain and Howard searched for elephant, in those moments I must have died a thousand deaths and as often mentally checked my first-aid kit, from morphia to antiseptic. Being with them was fine; waiting for them was sheer agony. After a week I had become less tense, less worried about their safety; a self-protective shell was slowly growing around me. Had we stayed another week or month it might have become a permanent fixture!

On the last day of the year, an elephant which Iain had named 'Mary's Toto' was darted at 16.46 hours in the right leg. It received a fairly large dose of M99 and went down in eleven minutes. The dart had been well placed, the drug had at last done its work swiftly and efficiently. But even then success was days away. As luck would have it, the darted male did not slow down as so often happens, but moved on, amidst the herd until it suddenly dropped. The nearest cow was alarmed at once and with one loud trumpet call alerted the whole herd which came to investigate the cause of the commotion. By the time the radio signal reached us and we hurried to the spot, the earth was alive with stamping, dust-throwing, screaming, trampling elephants, tearing up clumps of bushes in their fury, sixty in all, the earth-shaking eruption being the combined effort of two herds. Iain and Toni were making valiant efforts to move them by backing the Land-Rover towards them. The result was an immediate and intense renewal of infuriated charges, not half-hearted threats but the real thing. Nothing could have moved that protective barrier away from the recumbent elephant. Standing rump to rump as if sealing the rest of the world from the incapacitated male, they seemed to take it in turn to try and revive him. Using their tusks, they lifted him several feet off the ground time and time again then let him fall back on the ground after each unsuccessful attempt.

Far from trying to help him, they were surely going to kill or to severely injure him! We had moved to a respectful distance, observing the incredible demonstration, living evidence of the kind of behaviour which had so often been accredited to elephant—yet rarely recorded.

The sun was sinking low. From where we waited, looking on with our binoculars, the scene was something out of another world, the actors hardly real. Their conscious duty towards each other, their close-knit community, their ability to unite in a few moments to form an angry guard without a chink in its armour was something of a revelation. After an hour one part of the herd, which was a complete group in itself, left, and with it the mother of the immobile male. As they moved off the other group took over the vigil, a few of the eldest continuing to stir and move the recumbent form. Had the cow found the strain too great? Had the rest taken her away for solace and for food and water? We could never be sure. When they returned after thirty minutes, the cow again took charge of her son, the others once more becoming part of the encirclement. Part of the turmoil and constant cries of distress, at times so human that it could only be described as macabre, was caused by the younger generation milling and pushing between and among the adults, their behaviour very like that of a group of busybodies revelling in the excitement of the occasion.

Just over two hours after the elephant had been darted, we noticed that the sounds of war and the clouds of dust were getting less. The trunks were stiller, the screams that rent the air much fewer; could it be that the situation was resolving itself in some way or other? Our great concern was for the elephant, for we felt sure it would be trampled to death. When we saw it rise, sink back, rise again, try harder, and finally get on to its feet, we could hardly believe it. How, except by extremely good organization and complete lack of panic, could the elephant have escaped being trodden underfoot? Under similar circumstances man has been known to react very differently and with less thought for his fellow.

This was part of the mystery of the elephant; the puzzle that had never been solved. Their mystical conception of death, their necessity for a close-knit community, their methods of communication which were still largely matters for conjecture.

'All things come to him who waits,' the saying goes. And so, also, success at last came to us. New Year had come and gone, we hardly had time to notice it. On January 3rd, early in the morning, 'M43,' the elephant which had been darted but had been lost when he gained the dense forest, was spotted again.

This time Toni used more M99 and the dose took effect. He had come to the conclusion that Manyara elephants were tougher, different in their reaction, perhaps even different in other ways from the elephants he had so successfully immobilized elsewhere in Africa. Slowly he had increased the dose, making detailed notes of each elephant's reaction as it was darted. M43 took over an hour to go down and when he did, he went down fighting. He swayed, he circled, he resisted the effects of immobilization as no other elephant had ever done before. Once we even feared that he was showing signs of recovery and would yet escape us. As he rocked back and forth, still mobile, Toni crept up behind him and seized his tail in an effort to push him off balance and force him to sit down. Finding he could not influence the 8,000-pound bulk, he removed the dart from the flank in case the elephant should fall on it. I watched, as I always did such foolhardy but perhaps necessary escapades, with my overtaxed heart in my mouth.

We sprang into action as soon as we saw him sink on to his brisket. Howard was ready with the collar and placed it round his neck almost as soon as the elephant touched ground. He had prepared the needles and nylon tape, the thermister and sun-resistant pad, and as soon as the collar was firmly round the neck, he was on his back opening, inserting, and closing the wound. I was behind him trying to assist, ready to pull him off the elephant's back should he try to rise. Toni had placed a looped rope round the off-side tusk, ready to pull him over on to the side and off the brisket position which could cause death unless changed within fifteen or twenty minutes of going down. Iain, sitting in the Land-Rover to which he had already attached the rope, was waiting for Toni's signal to pull the elephant over. He revved the engine and moved slowly forward with the gear in low ratio, but this had little effect on the elephant except to disturb him so that he tried to rise. Eventually by rocking it from side to side, the rope and Land-Rover managed to pull the huge form over. I began to take blood from an ear vein while Toni prepared the compound which would antagonize the immobilizing dose. I found a few ticks for the parasitologists and made some blood slides, but that was all there was time for. Toni shouted a warning to return to the Land-Rovers and injected the antidote into a vein. After some moments the elephant slowly stirred and rose to his feet, complete with collar and body temperature transmitter. We collected ourselves and our equipment and watched him. After ten minutes a long official Parks Land-Rover drove up and out of it stepped no less a person than the Director of Parks, the dynamic John Owen, several visiting German members of Parliament and Professor Walter Russell, renowned agriculturist from Britain and one-time Director of the East African Agriculture and Forestry Research Organisation, who had come to advise on the future planning of Parks in Tanzania.

'Would you, Doctor Harthoorn, be kind enough to explain to these gentlemen something about the purpose of your work?' Toni could not have been more pleased, nor could Iain or I. We knew that one of the reasons for Professor Russell's visit was the dilemma over the Serengeti elephants. Should they, or should they not, be reduced in number, in view of the damage they were thought to be inflicting to the trees?

Toni took his cue. With complete sincerity and more clearly than I have ever heard him explain his work, he put forward his thoughts on elephant research. 'Before man may even consider curtailing the elephant populations he must find out something more about them than he knows at this time. This is what we are here for. The collar will transmit signals which Iain will be able to pick up. For the first time he will be able to follow night as well as daytime movement. The temperature signals will tell us more about the normal function of the elephant and from there we shall go on, searching, so that in the end we can truly say we know something about what the elephant does and how he does it . . .'

That late afternoon, while Iain, Toni and I went to attend to a sixteen-foot-high denizen of the Park, Howard and Dorothy set out to follow the collared elephant through the darkening jungle. The wireless sender was broadcasting its message and the antenna ready to receive. The Baldwins, rewarded at last, now longed to pluck the fruits of their endeavours, in spite of the obvious hazard of moving through thick country at night, especially without Iain as guide and protector. I tried to persuade them not to stay out too long. As the shadows lengthened, I grew more and more worried, for in Africa the forest becomes a hostile element for man as soon as light fades.

Upon our return after dark, and as we rounded the last bend along the path to Iain's camp, we suddenly came upon the Baldwins driving out in search of us! Amazed and delighted to see them safe and sound, we listened to the story of their evening's adventure. They told of their arrival in the forest at gathering dusk and how they located M43. He had moved some distance from where we had left him, but was still alone. Soon afterwards, however, he joined up with a large and aggressive herd which, unused to nightly visitors, made it clear that they did not appreciate the intruders. Gradually they closed in like great, grey battleships advancing upon their frail Land-Rover from all sides. The Baldwins vividly described their intense feeling of isolation among the vast, milling herd, and their growing realization that they must leave for camp before their way became irretrievably blocked. Howard, who not many days before had declared that working with elephants must be as easy as with lions, now freely admitted that he had been nervous and very frightened. Night tracking was not for him, he said with emphasis, not now nor at any other time; not unless Iain, who knew the herds so well, went with him.

We could not stay much longer to help Iain track his elephant as we had to return home via the Serengeti. We hoped to continue later in the year, armed by our week of experience. I lost my bet about the collar which proved how little I had as yet learnt about elephant. He did not try to remove it, or even to interfere with it. We were told how the other elephants came to admire it, how they touched it, one by one, with gentle reverence. When Iain came to stay with us in Nairobi one month later, it was still in place, still transmitting its directional signals. Iain was the happiest biologist alive, and the luckiest; and the best part of it was that he was fully aware of it.

14 *Twenty Thousand Elephants*

STRANGE THAT THE GIANTESQUE, pacifist lord of the jungle, who wants to live and let live, should be the one to set off a kaleidoscope of emotions ranging from fierce protectiveness to a violent, compelling desire to hunt and destroy him. He had inspired the greatest, fiercest wildlife controversy of the twentieth century. Others were being fought in distant parts of the world, but in East Africa he was the kingpin of discussion and of stormy disagreement.

It had come to a head about the time we were due to arrive in Kenya, the elephant rumblings having already reached us in the West of the United States. On the way we had stopped off in Scotland to attend the International Biological Symposium. Someone had thrust a newspaper in front of Toni, pointing to the headlines which read: 'Plan to slaughter 5,000 elephants in Tsavo National Park.' 'And what,' said the accusing voice, as if Toni were utterly responsible, 'what are *you* going to do about that? Surely you scientists are not going to stand by and allow mass murder to be committed without a prior investigation.'

It was no use explaining that the fate of the elephant was in other hands, that we had been quite out of touch with wildlife activities in East Africa for over six months. Had Toni attempted to justify himself to the belligerent gentleman from Britain, he would probably have ended up by admitting that his responsibility *was* as great as the next man's. Anyone with a voice which might be heeded, anyone who had some knowledge of the elephant problem, was duty bound to try and arrest the threatened large-scale culling.

My new father-in-law, a retired political economist with leanings towards wildlife rather than economics, had written us the same sad tale. He demanded—thereby showing absolute confidence in his son's capabilities to perform miracles—that he put a stop to the projected slaughter at once, implying that it must be done as we arrived and before we even began to unpack. 'He is quite right about the unpacking part,' I concurred sadly.

Toni, among others, had been asked to state his views on the Tsavo Park controversy. 'We must remember that at least part of the overcrowding in Tsavo has arisen because elephant have been astute enough to seek sanctuary in the Park from all manner of hunting,' he was quoted as saying. 'Unless elephant cropping is done with care and with knowledge based on trial and observation, we may find that the elephant will escape *out* of the Park and create a problem of entirely different dimensions.' Toni was also certain that the nutritional problems would be solved by management other than cropping, such as fire control, for instance.

'When your interview appears we shall be given a one-way ticket and asked to leave,' I predicted gloomily. 'Pity, I would love to have seen even a few of the 20,000 and the Tsavo National Park.'

Strangely enough, I couldn't have been more wrong for not long afterwards a further investigation was set up with the result that a new statement was issued. This time it was freely admitted that nothing would be decided on until research was carried out and that a team of scientists would assess elephant destruction and other causes of damage to the habitat. It was hoped that parallel vegetational studies would also be embarked upon, for without them the whole basis of the problem would remain obscure.

This new attitude was progressive and sensible. Nothing could be better for the elephant than to conduct research which would throw light on his ecological role. No one could

217

be certain if he were, indeed, multiplying too rapidly or devastating his habitat. The grant for an extensive study period was substantial. It meant that a botanist and other specialists could be employed and that aerial work would be possible. The world, almost as concerned over the elephant populations as Africa itself, settled down to await the findings of the research team, satisfied that, at last, the Tsavo question was being sorted out.

David Sheldrick, Warden of Tsavo East National Park, had, meanwhile, discovered some amazing facts; the elephant who was being accused by some of destroying his own larder, as it were, was probably not doing so at all. David, who had virtually created and planned this, the largest of all African animal sanctuaries, out of a hostile, harsh poacher-ridden wilderness, naturally wanted to know what was happening. If the vegetation were threatened too severely, steps would have to be taken to rectify the situation. He would, however, after twenty years of arduous, conscientious conservation, see to it that no elephant head would roll unless the reasons were sound, proven and the course inevitable.

Scientists of the calibre needed for such an enormous and exacting project were in very short supply. A man, prepared to live in the 'outback' of Africa, one who would submerge himself entirely in his work, who would sort out the elephant puzzle with complete dedication, such a man might be very difficult to find. He would have to be endowed with patience and love for wildlife, as well as scientific open-mindedness. He would have to use carcases made available by hunters and those who have to crop herds when agriculture is threatened. Above all, he would have to be a man prepared to share his findings *and* tissues with other scientists all over the world, for only in that way could needless slaughter be prevented.

The method embarked upon, however, was disappointing. An accepted way of working with small animals, such as rodents (which are not easily seen in their natural state and which are of little aesthetic value), is to kill numbers of a population. Reproductive rates and ageing are then determined from the carcases. Surely the elephant, without whom Africa could hardly be imagined, deserved a different approach. Whatever course this would take, it would have to be determined by prior observation and not by prior killing. Observing the elephant would not be an easy task, for he moves vast distances at surprising speed and at quite unexpected times. Aerial counts, conducted even at regular intervals, *could* be inaccurate. A few hundred could mount to thousands, it was easy to make mistakes.

The effects of fire had to be carefully considered right at the start of the research programme. Areas of elephant denudation were great, trees doomed to die from debarking were many. But then so were the forests that had been charred and blackened. Above all, the reseeding of trees was prevented because young saplings were destroyed by grass fires. In pastoral areas where, because of overgrazing, there is no grass to burn, the land eventually turns into bush and is likely to remain so unless the elephant moves in. By opening up patches of bush he makes it possible for the grass to grow. When this becomes long and dry, fires tend to break out more easily which constantly encroach on bush and forest, thereby extending the grassland.

If fires could be kept out of Tsavo, it may well be that elephant would be needed to stop it becoming a dense tangle of bush with consequent eradication of plains game, such as zebra. Before the effects of fire were fully studied and the impact on vegetation understood, it would not only be criminal but also dangerous, to begin to kill the elephant. Frank Fraser Darling, the world-famous ecologist, raised just this question at a wildlife meeting. 'After all,' he said, 'what is destruction, ecologically speaking? In the much bigger context of the eco-cycle, the elephant is merely doing what he has always done and is, in effect, "gardening".'

Iain Douglas-Hamilton had already discovered that the elephant was an excellent forester and that he, in fact, reseeded his own forests. When he pulled down the branches and ate the seeds, he spread them long distances away in an ideal condition to germinate. Pulling down tree limbs and whole trees might *seem* wasteful, yet the elephant was looking after his habitat in a most ingenious way. The fallen branches were protecting the soil which was sending out new growth, thus allowing the grass to seed itself before the grazers and rooters disturbed the process. After all, the elephant's diet is mostly derived from grass, though this fact had not been fully appreciated until recent years.

Only a few people in East Africa knew the real truth about the Tsavo situation; albeit not scientists, their observations had been of the highest scientific standards. Twenty years ago, when David Sheldrick was first appointed as a warden, the vegetation had consisted almost entirely of thick commiphora bush; so thick was it in fact, that one had difficulty in seeing more than a few yards on either side of the road. Plains animals were few and far between. About 1956 the elephant started knocking down the commiphora in some areas, and attention was drawn to the destruction of these trees. After a series of drought years, culminating in the rhino disaster of 1960, when some 350 rhino died of hunger and thirst in a forty-mile stretch of river, the country looked like a battlefield with fallen trees and baked bare earth, the situation did indeed seem very serious. Several eminent scientists were called in and were of the opinion that the elephant were destroying the habitat. It was thought that the rainfall was insufficient to sustain good grassland and that the end result would be desert. The main concern was that the rhino would be the hardest hit, and that whereas elephant are represented in almost every Park in Africa, black rhino were on the way out, and every effort must therefore be made to halt the trend in order to protect the rhino. There seemed to be no alternative but to reduce the elephant population as soon as possible, and a plea was made for a scientific investigation as a matter of urgency.

Several years later, the Range Management people were busy removing the bush by mechanical means just over the Park border; much to everyone's astonishment, good perennial grassland emerged. Where once there had been commiphora woodland with little or no cover underneath, grass plains country was emerging with a carrying capacity far greater than before. Doubt arose as to whether in fact the experts had not been too hasty in predicting a desert, for there was no reason why the devastated sections of the Park should not follow the same pattern as the Range Management area. The whole picture had changed; there were definite indications that grassland was emerging from the wreckage. Fallen trees channelled water into the ground and provided shade, up came the grass and with the help of good rains soon colonized huge areas. And with the grass sprang up sun-loving legumes favoured by rhino and other browsers. This opening up of the bush resulted in a very noticeable increase of plains animals, yet there was no sign of stress among the elephant themselves as a result. In fact, wherever possible, they ate grass in preference to bush. Numerous little springs appeared, providing permanent water. It seemed almost as though the commiphora, a greedy feeder, may have taken more than its fair share of moisture from the earth and that, as there was little cover underneath this bush, the run-off was terrific. The grass remedied this tendency, and the rain that fell seeped into the soil and replenished the water table instead of running off and forming roaring red torrents in the gulleys.

Those who had agitated for immediate measures to reduce the elephant population were now convinced that perhaps this was the wrong thing to do; that perhaps *the elephant were in fact improving the habitat.* Certainly the rapid build up of plains game was astonishing. Buffalo, zebra, oryx and many other species congregated in large herds and could be easily seen in the open country. In fact, from a tourist angle, there was no doubt that the Park had improved. Perhaps a natural cycle was being witnessed, grassland being the climax vegetation and not the commiphora. Delving back in old records, it was found that this area may well have been grassland in bygone days; had been overgrazed by domestic stock (the presence of ancient Galla graves would seem to support this theory), which resulted in bush encroachment, tse-tse fly, etc., driving the stock out in

turn and attracting the elephant! Now the elephants were
completing the cycle and turning the bush country into grassland again.

One August, without so much as an announcement in
scientific or wildlife journals, 300 elephants were destroyed.
Efficient, quick, whole herds at a time. Their skin, processed
and dyed, would serve as seat-covers for the smartest cars.
Shades of green, red, grey, black and tan, anything the market
might demand and pay for, would become available. Hippo
skins had already paid handsome dividends, now it was the
turn of the elephant. A new storm began to rage as soon as the
news leaked out. Why had no one been informed? Why was so
much material wasted? Why could more scientists not have
shared the tissues, that were needed all over the world for
various studies, many of which would ultimately benefit mankind as well? After all, one would have thought that the object
of the exercise was the enhancement of scientific knowledge!

This time science itself came under fire. If this was the way
men of science worked, then surely there was something very
wrong with the whole species. Some wondered why others
fussed over a mere 300 when the lives of 5,000 were at stake.
It seemed very strange to us, when not long before we had
waited for three anxious hours to see whether *one* young
elephant would survive the ministrations of the herd in
Manyara. When he had eventually got to his feet, whole and
unhurt, we had rejoiced, not only for him but because there
was, at least, one man among the few who wanted to preserve
while he was studying, not destroy.

The Tsavo team claimed that 300 specimens were vital for
the continuance of the survey. When the murmurings reached
their ears they complained that they were being interfered
with, that no self-respecting scientist can have success if he is
being eternally disturbed by those 'outside' the field who knew
nothing of the whys and wherefores of his activities. They gave
assurances that no havoc or disturbance had been caused by
the removal of a few herds. They had been killed with the aid
of a helicopter with a minimum of fuss. Then they had been

'processed' and removed by lorry. No one would ever be able to tell, they said, that 300 creatures had been destroyed.

In July 1967 a conference of Wildlife Management and Land Use had been called in Nairobi, attended by some overseas scientists, though mostly botanists, biologists, agriculturalists, wardens, rangers and wildlife officials from East Africa. The utilization of the good Mother Earth for the benefit of mankind was the theme. Was man really putting in a maximum effort so that everything that could be achieved in all fields of agriculture and wildlife management was being achieved? That included all the various aspects of animal and plant research and the adaptation of man and animal to his environment.

The concentration of wildlife orientated participation was very high. Coffee-break discussions were abuzz with elephants and cropping themes. The mass destruction in Tsavo, even though statistically the number actually killed may not have exceeded one per cent, had reached far and wide, in spite of attempted secrecy. Perhaps it had been that very attempt to hush it out of existence that had caused the greatest stir. It was rumoured abroad that there had been considerable profits and that these did not benefit science alone. Ian McTaggart Cowan, the world-renowned zoologist, had been very outspoken on the subject and had decried profit-making scientific projects.

'When vested interests,' he had said in his brilliant and very positive address, 'are allowed to influence the management policies of the National Parks, then you have placed your feet on the primrose path to disaster.'

Had this secrecy, this inability to share knowledge, been just another symptom of that trait so aptly described by Robert Ardrey in his book, *The Territorial Imperative*? It seemed that the clan of wildlife investigators in East Africa fitted most aptly into his description of the man whose '. . . human brain exceeds by far the potentialities of that possessed by any other animal species, its psychological processes probably differing *not at all* from those of animals.'

Even Phil Glover, the eminent plant ecologist, whose mildness and equanimity were as well recognized as his scientific achievements, finally blew his top. He announced, insisting that it be recorded for posterity, that personalities were bedevilling the cause of wildlife of East Africa. Were they then forgetting, in the pursuance of their individual goal, that wildlife is fragile and perishable, as Frank Minot put it, and that man, by his folly, is capable of destroying resources much more efficiently now than ever before. The earth's treasures, of which the elephant is one, must be preserved. We cannot just blow them off the face of the earth, beginning at Tsavo, under the guise of science, for once it is done, nothing will ever bring them back. As they stand in their thousands, they can yet be studied as a whole, a moving, fantastic treasure house of knowledge. Landing at the air-strip of the Serengeti National Park, one is forced to face the truth almost at once. A beautifully carved notice board has been placed in such a way that everyone must see it:

TANZANIA NATIONAL PARKS
HERE THE WORLD IS STILL YOUNG AND FRAGILE
HELD IN TRUST FOR YOUR SONS AND OURS

There was a stir among the audience when D. F. Vesey-Fitzgerald, the Warden of Ngurdoto Crater National Park in Tanzania stated from the platform that his problem was in direct opposition to that of the elephant eradicators. 'You see, ladies and gentlemen,' he said, beaming at us, 'my problem is *how to keep the elephants in rather than how to keep them out.*' Vesey, his sensitive, artistic face aglow whenever he spoke of his elephants, described his Park and its inhabitants. It was richly endowed with many kinds of vegetation and scenery, including the game-filled crater, the forests, woodland and lakes. To me, who had not yet seen it, it sounded very like a twenty-square-mile paradise, containing animals and birds in great profusion. Sir Julian Huxley had spoken of it as 'a little gem'; Vesey protected it and all it enfolded like a sort of St. Francis—in fact, when I looked at him through half-closed eyes as he spoke, he seemed to become transformed into the animal saint.

'In Ngurdoto we work with the animals and not against them,' he said, almost apologetically: yet his shy, self-effacement contained all the power and irresistible force which only a man of his calibre, a biologist as well as warden, could transmit across the rows of listening faces. Vesey, whose problems were very different and far smaller than those in the Tsavo National Park, had built an electric fence to keep his elephants in, a vital factor for their protection since three sides of Ngurdoto were surrounded by cultivation. To get his herd used to the fence had not been easy; as one might expect, they had had their fun with it. Still, in the end, and up to the time of telling, they had remained within the barrier but only because their guardian had not lost patience with them. While he watched their behaviour, their reaction to the 'psychological barrier' as he called it, he made observations about their social and individual life patterns and found them, as Iain Douglas-Hamilton had done, the most engrossing subjects for study. When Vesey-Fitzgerald sat down after his oration there was universal and prolonged applause. Prolonged, perhaps, partly because the need for parks and sanctuaries was growing daily. Since it was predicted that by 1975 there would be 4,000 million people on earth, one could assume that a great number of them would be in need of asylum to restore their equilibrium and cramped sensibilities. Man was already in desperate need of a natural tranquillizer, something which would give him a glimpse into a world which is closer to his own inherent nature. Could it not be that the magnificent spectacle of wild animals, such as the 20,000 elephant in Tsavo National Park, could form an essential link between him and his saner self?

It was not solely a case of ecological balance, proper and economic land use for its own sake or preservation of the wild, important as these are. It would soon be a matter of life and death to millions to know that somewhere, within their reach, there was a corner of the earth which would provide them with a respite from the terrifying rat-race of the insatiable modern world. As Toni put it so aptly in his foreword to John Sinclair's book, *Twilight*, which described the threatened wealth of Africa: 'It may well be that now is the moment for Mankind to get away from the laboratory bench and the drawing board and to turn back to some of the fundamental truths of biology, for some comprehension and reassurance.'

15 *No Tracks in the Sea*

I COUNTED MYSELF most fortunate to have, indeed, entered a world where the fundamental truths of biology were being studied—in every sense of the word.

Our existence had become so wholly orientated to African animals that work with and for them seemed an end in itself. The greater was our surprise when, during a sojourn in the United States, Toni was asked to join a 'killer' whale expedition in the San Juan Islands off Portland, Oregon, as immobilizer of the operation. Toni had given a series of lectures in American Universities which dealt largely with his own aspect of physiological work. During these he showed his slides, taken over the years, demonstrating most vividly the purpose and achievements of large animal chemical restraint. The enthusiasm and interest of the students and staff was overwhelming; to them wildlife spelt the romance of the African continent, the reason why so many flocked to East Africa. The slide of a huge standing savanna elephant, from which Toni was extracting a dart, brought expressions of amazement to their lips. A heavily tranquillized zebra being ridden, a marked hippopotamus being 'launched' back into Lake George after the antidote had been administered captured their interest completely. The danger, the heartaches, the patience of the men who made it possible could not be transmitted. On the contrary, Toni always made light of the hardships and concentrated on the highlights, for he wanted only to put across what could be achieved by these new methods in the field of conservation.

227

From the back of the hall, where I usually sat, I observed the reactions of the audience and tried to judge whether or not they could understand everything that Toni, with his ten-syllable word usage, put across. 'A little mystery makes for added interest,' he used to say. 'If they understand *everything* they will think it very queer.' Most Americans did think us a little odd, in any case. We spoke strangely, looked, according to one of our Canadian friends, 'like a pair of giraffe' by virtue of our height and enthused about hippopotamus which bit Land-Rovers in half. Apart from being tall we had giraffe-like vegetarian eating habits, horrifying host after host by refusing the tenderest steak or crispest chicken, whichever happened to be the pride of that part of the country. It depended a little on the location we happened to be in, for the people varied enormously in knowledge, habit and accent from state line to state line.

Some, hearing our accents and discovering we hailed from 'darkest' Africa simply assumed that we were mission-aries. Others looked upon us as a sort of pioneering couple who had donned clothes specially for our trip to the United States. We were asked about Doctor Leakey, the Adamsons and the Serengeti and when Toni admitted that he had a nodding acquaintance with all three they were more than a little impressed.

'And now I will show you a picture of a rare mammal, seen sporadically in various game parks throughout Africa, that must under no circumstances be approached unless entirely tranquil.' I could hear the indrawing of breath as he made this portentous statement, some gripping their seats with anti-cipation. My heart sank; poor students, poor disappointed staff and professors, for all they were about to see—to my chagrin—was a slide of myself dressed in the skimpiest imaginable shorts, emerging from a game park hut. However great their disappointment may have been, they always responded with hearty laughter—and, I thought at times, relief, for this meant the end of the lecture and the beginning of question time.

'Have you worked on any of the sea mammals?' someone had once asked him in the West of America. That had been before the invitation to join the marine expedition had been issued and had given us much room for thought.

The large sea mammals, threatened with extinction even more surely than many African animals, would have to be studied before they could be scientifically conserved. At least that much applied equally to both. How one would go about capturing an immense whale who left no tracks to be followed was something else again, especially when man, who was already handicapped on land, would be entirely out of his element at sea. Marine biologists had made immense progress and were delving more and more deeply into the mystery of the underwater creatures. Doctor Sheville, of Woods Hole Oceanographic Institution, who had generously sent us his record of underwater sounds, had achieved great success in recording the fantastic, most unearthly sounds of sea inhabitants. The language of the Right Whale, however, had something very African about it and just to prove it we used to play it to our friends, many of them authorities on wildlife, selecting the sound but excluding the explanatory dialogue. 'Sounds like a hippo,' some said, 'like the muted belly roar of a lion,' said others, but no one ever guessed that the fearsome base vocalization had been produced by a whale and recorded deep under water!

Toni took some of his M99 and the antidote M285 to San Juan. Doctor Mayberry, the veterinarian from the Portland Zoo, brought darts and other equipment. The boats, helicopter and accommodation were taken care of by the instigators of the operation, the MacLaughlin brothers. Toni spent several weekends with them, and I joined them for just a few days, sufficient to give me a taste of the most exciting work of which I had yet been a part. Toni was just as enthralled as I was, for the sight of the elusive and highly intelligent sea monsters, non-aggressive, though they no doubt suspected our intentions, was something more wonderful even than the sight of a herd of elephant.

Sitting on the prow of the main operational boat, we witnessed hours and eventually days of the most exciting interplay between man and animal. This time the whale was the behaviourist, for his observations seemed to give him the advantage over us each and every time. The helicopter seemed clumsy compared to the lightning grace of the shining black, white-bellied giants, who pitched and tossed and finally 'sounded' (went under water) with split-second timing whenever the helicopter came within range. Exactly at the moment when it turned away, the marksman still at the ready, the six-foot fins and twenty-ton bodies would appear again, playing all about us with triumphal ecstasy. If at first we had not been certain of their intent, we were left in no doubt by the end of three days of anxious waiting, watching and planning. Each time the team thought of a new way to outwit them, the herd responded with an even quicker plan of escape. I got the firm impression that they did not really ever take us very seriously. On the last day the herd bull, a huge whale whose eyes seemed to regard us with at least human intelligence, led us to believe, by creating a tremendous commotion, that he was part of the herd while in actual fact they 'blew' (rose to the surface) some minutes later about one mile away!

Strange that so many tales had been passed on through the centuries about the killer whale, each one adding something more to the accounts of his ferocious man-eating tendencies. According to one report he stopped at nothing, following man even on to iceflows and other obstacles. He swallowed porpoises whole by the dozen, it was true, and, in fact, anything else that got in his way. But to accuse him of aggressiveness, of killing merely for the sake of it, seemed most unjustified; one had only to watch his playfulness at close quarters when he had ample opportunity to strike, to realize that he was neither vicious nor vindictive.

If elephant had ever made us feel small, then these twenty-tonners made us feel infinitesimal. It gave Toni a feeling of tremendous urgency to work for the conservation of whales which meant that they had to be immobilized and instrumented. Operation San Juan had not proved successful, but it had certainly not been a waste, for perhaps some time in the future we would be able to return and continue—provided there would be any of the larger whales left alive to work on.

'You haven't seen anything yet,' one of the boat crew had told us during my weekend there. 'Go and see the blue whale in the Smithsonian Institute.' Having been invited to partake in the bi-centenary Smithsonian celebrations in Washington, D.C., we had the opportunity to go to visit the incredible life-size model of this mammal, the largest on earth. On the background wall, dolphins and other whales had been painted, tiny compared with even the head. 'He is a very pacifist sort of creature, like all the baleen whales,' Hal Beuchner, the Assistant Director of Ecology at the Institute and our host, had said; he had shown us the strange pleats under the mouth, as if the vast underside could be inflated with food. He was not a voracious feeder like the killer whale, but filtered sea-water as he went along. Like many of the larger land mammals, he was also threatened with extinction, victim of man's greed and inability to see into the future.

On the day we saw the mighty whale replica and the halls of scientific and other exhibits, which we could have spent weeks visiting and studying, we also met George Schaller, the German-American zoologist, whose young face and slight figure belied the burning energy and single-mindedness with which he was possessed. I always thought that, but for his stabilizing, gentle, very beautiful wife, George, tense and highly strung, would many times have gone up in smoke. While Jimmy, Hal's wife, showed me where I could most wisely spend our few remaining dollars, Hal, George and Toni got down to some scientific discussion. George had already made an outstanding contribution to biology with his work on the gorilla in the Congo and the tiger in India, and was about to leave for the Serengeti to study the African lion. He hoped that Toni would be able to help with immobilization, for without it George could not begin to mark individuals for his ecological and behavioural investigations. We were then on the point of leaving for Kenya, the Schallers travelling to their new base in Tanzania three months later.

In spite of the fact that we were about one year late, when we finally visited George in Serengeti, they had given us a warm welcome when we arrived, forgiving and forgetting all our shortcomings with a smile and a handshake. It had been my first visit to the Serengeti and I had at last witnessed the migrations of the great herds, had been part of them as we had driven in from the north. It would be hard to describe the feeling of wonder as we saw the green plains turn black with the milling, vocalizing, switch-tailed thousands moving in one direction [*Endpapers*] and with only one aim. Sometimes they broke line and stood, in protective circles, resting their young while keeping a wary eye on the ever-hungry camp-followers, the hyena and lion. Zebra, antelope and gazelle lightened the grey-black galaxy of seething, stamping wildebeest on the move, estimated that year to be about 350,000 in number. From the air, from which we were able to observe it all much more clearly, they appeared like the last exodus, leaving man's domain for a better, more peaceful world.

Some of George Schaller's lions (the ones he had already tagged and was studying), were nomadic and left to follow the herds. Others, more strictly territorial stayed in or near their old hunting grounds protecting their land, which ranged from fifty to sixty square miles per lion. Watching the behaviour of lions was a long-term and very slow study, for two-thirds of a lion's life is spent in sleep. George, an ardent and enthusiastic scientist, hardly ever allowed himself to rest. He was out in the plain, in the forest, observing, tagging, instrumenting almost seven days of every week. The Serengeti National Park contained 6,000 square miles, a vast area for any research project. Though much of this was plains land, with rocky outcrops rather than trees, he often found that whole parties had disappeared within the space of perhaps half an hour while he had taken a nap in his Land-Rover.

By the time we brought George Adamson to see him he had already made tremendous progress in his work. Many of his observations had been unexpected and unusual, for the lions of the Serengeti seemed very different from the more active members of the species in other parts of East Africa, such as Tsavo or even Meru. George had found that they often stole the kills of hyena, quite a turn about from the accepted lion kill-hyena scavenge pattern. Among other things, he was observing the effect of lion predation on prey population and had tagged 150, putting radio-telemetric directional collars on some of them, which, like the elephant study, would give a much clearer indication of their day-to-day movement. He knew many by sight through scars, broken tails and other injuries. On one afternoon when I had the good fortune to drive out with him, we saw twenty-four lions in three hours, of these five had injuries. We had already heard about the high mortality rate of the young, as high as sixty per cent. He had once taken us to watch a lioness, her new cub crying with hunger, while an older cub had been allowed to suck, growling and snarling at the rightful owner of the milk-bar whenever he approached. If mother-love was at such a low ebb, no wonder the cub would starve and die of nothing more or less than neglect! Yet perhaps it was also Nature's way of checking the reproductive potential, for George had already recorded the amazing feat of one pair of lions mating eighty-four times in the space of twenty-four hours.

We had brought the two 'lion-men' together, since George Adamson had decided that the time had come for him to take yet another step forward, and that, in fact, his own active part in the rehabilitation was nearing its end. His pride, composed of four growing cubs, as well as Girl, Boy and Ugas, were quite at home in their new surroundings, their growing independence a measure of his success. For two years he had kept detailed observations which he made available to anyone who cared to read them. His findings, which ranged from territorial display, sexual and social behaviour, predation and rearing of young, would be of tremendous importance to conservation.

The more the pride merged into their territory, the less need they had for their guardian; I could understand something of his feelings as his charges turned to him less and less for parental support and protection; whether child or lion, when the day of separation came, parting would always be 'sweet sorrow'.

George knew that, like Joy who was studying cheetah, he must keep a link with the pride so that he would not lose them altogether. He followed and often found them far from camp; yet the day would come when they might change their territory. To maintain their interest, he fed them whenever they returned, which gave him a chance to observe them more closely. The progress of the cubs was important; they had the advantage of pride shelter and protection, of being 'broken in' by their elders whose own rehabilitation had been much more difficult. Boy and Girl, and especially Ugas, had entered a territory which had to be fought for, and there had been no one but George to help: the cubs had a much easier time of it for the other three had already paved the way for them. Nevertheless, they had to learn to hunt and it was quite obvious that after a certain age no one was going to 'spoon feed' them. There could be wounds which might need attention, there could also be diseases which might attack them. They had been hand-raised at Naivasha, a lake area which might have left them without immunity against the dread diseases of the northern bush.

As opposed to the overall study in the Serengeti, the cares of the Meru pride were part of rehabilitation. Without keeping too close a link George had to be sure that he gave them a good start until they had run the initial gauntlet of bush trials. He sent us a copy of his reports and we were able to see the immense changes that were taking place. Girl had bred with wild lions as well as Boy and had now assumed full duties as a mother. Her natural possessiveness had given way to pride comradeship as she allowed Suki, grown to a young lioness, to help with the baby-sitting whenever she decided to take a break. She allowed George to sit and watch her family as if he was a close relative, observing lioness-cub behaviour which had probably never been recorded at close range before.

On one of our visits to Meru, Toni, George and I had put our heads together to try to find the answer. George really needed a biologist to advise him in the first place; someone who was experienced in behaviourist studies and had good contacts with scientific institutions. The obvious man to approach was George Schaller, and it was important that the two should meet so that 'Serengeti' George could acquaint himself with the type of study, and hence the type of man needed, in Meru. We had fixed upon a certain date for our journey, arranging to fly to Serengeti since Toni's time was so short. We sent a radio signal to the Park Headquarters in Arusha to warn our hosts of our imminent arrival, but then immediately reversed the message when we heard that 'Meru' George would not leave camp at Meru. Having made extensive arrangements for our departure, always onerous whether for two days or twenty, we were a little deflated and disappointed not to be able to leave. Still, it was only one week's postponement, and we had gained a marvellous weekend of peace since we had already cancelled all our social engagements and told everyone that we would be away.

The following Friday, having again radioed the Schallers that we were now really coming, I had a premonition that George would not arrive. Instead, a young Canadian friend of a friend blew in with tales of the two brown bears she brought for His Majesty the Emperor of Ethiopia, and having regaled us thus for one entire evening, we could do no less than ask her to sleep in the bed we had made up for George. By ten o'clock that night I was praying that my premonition had been correct, for the rains had well and truly come, excluding the outside cottage as a guesthouse, while the children's room, often used in emergencies, was in turmoil as Gail and Guy vainly searched for their truant Italian grass snake.

Eventually, after many adventures, George arrived from Meru three weeks late, looking amazingly fresh, neat and handsome as he walked through the front door. After all, who were we to judge a man less than one month behind time, when we ourselves had dared to ask the Schallers for hospitality after being expected for over a year! 'I do hope I haven't kept you waiting,' he said with such an apologetic, expectant smile that had he kept us in suspense for ten years I could not have brought myself to admit it!

'You are in excellent time and everything is laid on for tomorrow,' I said, to put his mind at rest. Perhaps the Schallers would not mind if we came after all; as long as we could get a plane to fly us at such short notice nothing else really mattered.

The journey over the Rift and the lakes had been worth every moment of waiting, for I had never before seen the valley in the early morning looking like the huge geological fault in the earth's crust that it really is. The clouds threw dancing shadows on the chasm below, its sides like jagged steps leading towards the mountains. Lake Magadi had appeared next, where tens of thousands of young flamingos had been ankle-cuffed by soda deposits years before and had had to be rescued. Lake Natron, breeding ground of the greater flamingo appeared next, the whole side section of the lake one pink scum of wings. After that I had not trusted myself to look to right or left, for the aircraft was rocking and pitching as the warm currents of air surged upwards. I had, in my morning rush, forgotten to eat breakfast and my stomach flayed about with horrible weightlessness. The sensation somehow involved the balancing mechanism of my inner ear, though how they could be connected was an enigma. 'I must ask Toni,' I thought, as I closed my eyes and went to sleep, a dreadful thing to do when the vastness of the Serengeti lay below us, a sight that half the world would give anything to see.

Getting the two lion Georges together was marvellous; each a specialist in his own field, they complemented each other perfectly. George Adamson, the elder of the two, was deferential to Schaller's superior scientific knowledge. The latter, roughly half his distinguished guest's age, admired and respected the experience of the ex-game warden's forty years of life in the bush. They compared notes on lion behaviour and George Adamson told of the days when, thirty years before, he had come to the Serengeti, then not established as a Park, for the sole purpose of photographing the famous lions. We went out to see something of George Schaller's territory of study and in the middle of a tremendous windstorm, drank tea in the tent, pitched beneath a lion kopje, where George often spent nights when following the prides. We found leopard draped in the trees rather in the manner of the Manyara lions, we saw a cheetah running off with a new-born tommy gazelle while the mother leapt about in a frenzy. We stopped to watch many of George's tagged lions, looking a little like something off a Christmas tree and heard of the controversy and criticism which had found its way to this study project because the tourists had objected to seeing lions which had been tampered with by man.

'I'll have to mark my pride one day,' George Adamson had said, 'it's the only way the tourists will know who they are. I could mark them myself with colour dye and perhaps the tourists, instead of resenting the marking, could be asked to report anything they have seen.' This meeting was for pre-liminary planning, for Meru George had yet to receive final sanction that he could go ahead with his scheme. George Schaller would help him all he could and would try and come to Meru Park to assess the situation, if only he had more time! Already with two years to go, he was dreading the moment when his four-year study period would end and he would have to return home to civilization.

I had a sudden vision of the two Georges, plunged from their present freedom into captivity, into the agony of hum-drum routine and blank mornings devoid of birdsong. Then my day-dream dissolved into the well-remembered image, a lion, newly caught, pacing hour after hour behind his iron bars. I shuddered at the memory, understanding perhaps for the first time . . .

16 *Not Only for Man*

'IF ONLY WE COULD STUDY extra-sensory perception one day,' Toni said with longing after our return from the Serengeti. 'Just imagine what an exciting new world would open up if we could receive the subtle radiations of the mind and the different parts of the human, animal and vegetable body. If we could measure the wavelengths of each cell-group we could find out infinitely more than, at the present time, I can discover with my clumsy radio-telemetric apparatus.'

We had discussed the subject before, but perhaps, until that moment, I had not been aware that, given the opportunity, Toni would one day devote himself to the research of radionics, the study of radiation, probably a two-way affair, which might enable man not only to receive but also to transmit his reactions to the animals. Fear and aggression, the barrier between animal and man might be overcome so completely that physiological enigmas could be unravelled without the aid of any immobilizing substance. I had had a curious and very wonderful experience not long after our return home which had set Toni thinking very deeply in this direction.

It had happened in Meru Park just before I was due to fly home. The new warden and his wife, Jean and Johnny Nesbitt, were valiantly entertaining six of us to lunch when one of the rangers entered with an urgent message for Johnny. He had spoken so quietly that I had only heard the reply. 'Poor little chap, we'll probably have to shoot him.' Joy Adamson sitting opposite me, had, however, heard it all.

238

'No, don't,' she had exploded in true Joy fashion; 'Sue will fix him!'

What faith she had, and here I was without Toni or any of the immobilizing drugs needed for even a preliminary examination. It was the first time I had ever flown to Meru alone. It was rather a strange experience and though Toni had been very disgruntled about my going off into the bush without him, I had, in the end, persuaded him that I should be allowed some independence for just that once.

'Let's go and see him before we take off,' I had said tentatively to the pilot who had arrived to fly us back to Nairobi. I was getting a 'lift' with a film team who knew quite well that the rhino enclosure was at least twenty minutes' drive away. 'It won't take long,' I pleaded. 'After all, the life of a giraffe is at stake. Either I can do something myself, which I doubt, or at least I can try to judge his condition and perhaps bring Toni back for help.' I looked at them all in turn; since Joy and George, Johnny and I were all equally anxious to do something, they could hardly refuse. Before they could remonstrate we were out and into Joy's Land-Rover and on the way towards the entrance gate.

The 'little' giraffe, who had voluntarily joined the rhino group was eight feet tall and about six months old. He was half tame, used to the rangers who took care of the rhino. Long eyelashes, sensitive face and beautifully marked, he stood alone in the corral, the rhino men behind him, keeping their aroused charges at bay with a stick. 'Murera', as the giraffe was called after a nearby river, had strayed into the pen of one of the fiercest, most possessive bulls who would not tolerate even an inter-species companionship for his mate. How the young giraffe had survived the attack was amazing; perhaps it was his comparatively small frame and weight which had saved him from fatal injury.

Without getting too near it was easy to see that his right front leg was bearing little weight and that he was in considerable discomfort if not pain, for the expression on his face was one of acute mistery and bewilderment. 'I'll go in alone,' I

239

said to the others, 'and see if I can get close enough to make a diagnosis.' To restrain him forcibly would have been a pity, especially as he would almost certainly struggle and further injure himself. I climbed through the fence and as I did so he slowly turned his head towards me, regarding me with a steady and unblinking gaze. I stopped in my tracks and tried to hold the attention of his eyes, and as I did so I sensed a feeling akin to fellowship, a sort of two-way trust such as one sometimes experiences with a complete stranger at the most unexpected times. Gradually, by moving very slowly and talking softly to him all the while, I reached the place where he stood and stopped in front of him, waiting for him to lower his head so that we could take a closer look at each other.

His eyes were enormous and soft, and I wondered idly whether anyone who had looked deeply into those dark brown pools would ever try to deny that giraffe have a soul. I touched his muzzle. It was the softest, most velvety surface I had ever felt. As the minutes ticked by I moved towards his right side and passed my hand over the shoulder and down the leg. The ranger, not many paces away, asked if he could help but I told him no, I thought it better to do this part on my own but that he should be sure to keep the rhino, who made periodic rushes towards us, well back near their own enclosure.

I began to palpate the shoulder, obviously the seat of injury, trying to establish how badly he was hurt. I watched his eyes and as I did so saw him wince and make a slight shuddering movement of his head and body. It was obviously very painful, yet he seemed not to resent me at all, acting as if he had, in fact, been immobilized. I bent the leg by holding the foot, and even that he bore without resentment, seeming to say: 'It's jolly sore, but I'll try not to make a scene and I know you'll do your best.'

Anthropomorphizing? Perhaps. However hard one might try, it is almost impossible to put into words what is transmitted from one being to another.

I diagnosed partial fracture, swelling, contusion and a small wound. I went back to the Land-Rover to get a syringe, needle, swab and antibiotic, for if I injected now I might be able to prevent infection of the bone and joint. When I returned to him, syringe in hand, his expression was far less serene and he began to move away with a painful hobble. I tried consciously to block my thoughts, as I had so often done with other animals, to invoke that feeling of tranquillity which had created such a definite bond only a few minutes before. When I realized that this wasn't possible I decided to make a clean breast of it, for I had the feeling that he was an unusually intelligent and very sensitive animal and might react more favourably if I was completely honest. 'I am going to inject you,' I said very quietly, 'so don't try to move away. I'll do it as quickly as I can.' Amazingly enough, as soon as I began to talk, he stopped, turned and took another look at my diminutive form. At that moment Johnny Nesbitt came up to help and as he held him for a moment I was able to inject the antibiotic through the toughest hide imaginable!

As soon as he felt the needle he shied away once more, his trust evaporated, the spell broken. I walked back to the fence, gave the syringe to someone to hold and begged them for a few more minutes. 'I want to win back his confidence; I cannot just leave him like this.' Then I asked the ranger for some fodder and went back step by step until he allowed me to come within a distance when he could reach my hand. He nibbled suspiciously at first, then, realizing that I really had finished the unpleasant part of our interview, he came close, and ate handfuls while I rubbed his neck and stiff short mane and bade him farewell. It was quite a wrench leaving Murera; I would have liked very much to spend at least a few hours with him, watching, communing, allowing our friendship to grow a little more.

'We'll look after him,' Johnny had promised. 'Just tell us what to do.' I suggested hot and cold applications to the swelling as often as three times a day, a place of his own for safety and peace of mind and high feeding and watering troughs so that he would not have to cause painful movement of the front leg and shoulder every time he ate and drank.

'Let me know, please, what happens through the Parks network,' I asked Johnny and Jean; 'if you need anything I'll send it up or come myself.'

That had been in October. Five months later, two days after the rhino had tracked five miles to their new paddocks in Leopard Rock, the little giraffe was killed. 'Dreadful news,' wrote Johnny in his report. 'Little Murera, the giraffe, who has been a companion to the rhino for over a year, who has miraculously escaped several attempts on his life by predators and a shoulder injury completely healed has finally succumbed to the harshness of Nature in the raw. He was killed by two lions within the paddock at 2 a.m. A delight to everyone who saw him, he is very sadly missed by those who knew and were associated with him.'

I was very grateful to be allowed to read the report. I already knew that Murera was dead, but what I didn't know and which I found a great consolation, was that others, like Johnny, who was far too busy to spend a great deal of time with the giraffe, had also regarded him as an individual, a personality in his own right, rather than just another member of the giraffe species. The words, 'very sadly missed by those associated with him', were a fitting epitaph which expressed exactly what I had felt about him: that he was a creature endowed with a certain almost human perception, something very special which is not usually attributed to animals at all.

When I returned home I told Toni about Murera even before I related my other adventures. He was so interested, so absorbed when I described the giraffe's reactions and behaviour that he forgot to scold me for taking unnecessary risks. 'Immobilization through a process of telepathic communication with animals, a kind of extra-sensory control, might one day be accepted as readily as radio-control is now,' Toni said. 'It's a dream, something for our old age.'

I was listening, enthralled, imagining the vast possibilities, yet realizing, as we both did, that without peace and mind control nothing even remotely extra-sensory could ever be achieved.

'Let's go to Kenplains,' Toni said suddenly, leaping off the settee. 'Let's go and see how my more realistic radio-receiving eland station is getting on!'

Leaving one's house after four o'clock would normally mean that one would not be in time for tea if the destination was still twenty miles away. At Kenplains, however, the farm home of the incredible Hopcraft family, it was different. Here, Sunday tea was an outdoor affair, sipped within sight of the mountain Lukenia and the endless rolling plains of the Athi. This was where Toni conducted his radio-telemetric work, using wild animals which were being ranched for study purposes.

As we drove up to the homestead we were met by Esther Hopcraft walking along with an assortment of dogs, and our ex-patient cheetah, who alternated between periods of panting exhaustion and breakneck sprints across the fields.

'You're in good time,' said Esther, her lovely, ever-welcoming face wreathed in smiles. 'I am just about to bring tea on to the lawn. We must get rid of the horse,' she said, as we entered the garden, 'he is such a nuisance and will insist on joining in at mealtimes.' The great chestnut had preceded us, next to him a minute meercat not reaching to his pastern, but behaving exactly as if he were at least twice as big as the horse. I was inclined to make a rush across the lawn to rescue him and wondered why no one else had thought of the same thing.

'He's fine, don't worry,' Jack Hopcraft said, as he emerged from the antelope enclosure with the visiting Denny family of eight. 'If anyone is going to get hurt it won't be Scrabble.'

Meanwhile the dachshund and black kitten had arrived and were met by a vicious, tooth-bared attack from the territorial Scrabble, who having dealt with them, then attacked Preech, who had arrived to join the fray. The little meercat, having repelled the canines and felines by means of his needle-sharp teeth, now attacked the horse from behind. Seeing that he did not create the desired effect, he backed, in typical meercat fashion, then charged forward again, interrupted this time by

Gail and Guy who, having once again spent the weekend on the farm, were well used to Scrabble's antics.

Toni, lying prone on his stomach, was trying his hardest to get some photographs of the steenbuck and the now full-grown cheetah, but whenever he clicked his camera a foot or hand or piece of flying fur obstructed his view. David Hopcraft appearing from the rear, took one look at the gathering, then wandered off towards the animal pens, inviting Toni to join him as soon as he had completed his photographic marathon.

Toni's radio-telemetry, which was an extramural activity, could not be conducted without the help of someone who had to be stationed at base camp, and who had to know not only how to control half-wild antelope and young buffalo, but how to grapple with the mysteries of the complicated radio-telemetric apparatus.

They had to be interested enough in the whole project to work *day and night*, taking readings of various physiological parameters, such as respiration, heart-beat and temperature. Radio-telemetry was one of the ways of measuring these processes without disturbing the animal. It involved initial immobilization and the introduction of an instrument which could, by means of a predetermined code, send back radio signals to a receiving set from which they were translated into actual figures. More broadly speaking, the overall purpose of this work was that of the study of the adaptation of wild animals to their environment and especially their reaction to stresses such as the sun's radiation and water shortage.

How, after all, does the hartebeest manage to stand in the hot African sun day after day without the regular intake of water? By allowing his temperature to rise, he need expend no water in sweating or panting. Also, by reducing the temperature difference between his body and the environment, less heat is absorbed. Human medicine, remote as it may seem from this aspect of research, would ultimately benefit a great deal, for a giraffe, telemetrized for blood pressure study, might reveal data which could be used for treatment of human hypertension (high blood pressure).

One of Toni's dreams (another one), was to make this project part of a wider, centralized scheme so that scientists with similar interests from other parts of the world could combine to expedite this urgent work.

Slowly, I too began to understand the implications and aspects of radio-telemetry but could be of little help since Toni needed someone at Kenplains as a semi-permanent fixture; even *had* I been mechanically minded enough to work for him, he would doubtlessly have objected to my absence from home. 'When are you going to find someone to help you?' I had asked as soon as he had joined forces with the David Hopcraft research scheme to the extent that they shared some of the animals.

'Have faith,' he had reprimanded me; 'something will drop out of heaven. Always does when we need it,' he added with terrifying certainty, terrifying for me for such categorical statements, based on *absolutely nothing but faith*, made me shudder.

I didn't have to shudder for very long. Within two weeks of his prediction, the sky did indeed pour forth its abundance. Not one, but *three* intelligent, adventurous, semi-scientifically minded and very well-proportioned young ladies appeared, one by one, as if by a miracle. They, metaphorically speaking, threw themselves at Toni's feet and begged him for work. They wanted to contribute something to African wildlife studies, they said, and would take a job with or without pay.

Virginia, a young scientist in her own right, was put in charge of operations, while Kendra, who was less experienced, was placed second in command. Pam, who had, unfortunately for her, an extraordinary aptitude for typing, lived with us, helping not only with Toni's work but also with mine, which included taming the children and keeping the telephone and visitors at bay.

Five months after the gay trio began their labour of love and just as the most exciting results were coming in, the heavy rains began to fall. This spelt temporary calamity for the project and drove Virginia and Kendra citywards to the veterinary laboratory where they spent hundreds of hours composing drawings, graphs and tables, end point of the practical investigations.

Toni's office and centre of operations was almost always alive with the buzz of voices and milling humanity. Endless matters of administration had to be solved, letters to dictate, students to console, technicians to direct, colleagues to consult, visitors to show around.

When time permitted, I joined Toni for mid-morning coffee and was fascinated by the white-coated activities of a highly organized pre-clinical veterinary department. When the rains became heavy and the sand-roads impassable, many field projects came to a halt. Dick Denney, whom we knew from our Colorado days, and who had come to Africa as part of the United Nations Range Management Team, had also stopped operations for the time being and sometimes joined Toni in his office, sitting patiently in the big armchair, waiting for the commotion to die down. Working closely with Toni who supplied him with immobilizing drugs, Dick marked hundreds of wild animals in different parts of East Africa by means of dart-syringes shot either from the ground in vehicles or from the air in helicopters. The latter, particularly, were often objects of great interest to the local people who would gather round after landing and question Dick as to his seemingly strange undertaking. In broader terms, David Hopcraft's antelope ranching study, Toni's more detailed radio-telemetry and Dick's project were closely linked. Dick wanted to determine the ebb and flow, the turnover of the wild herds from one location to another, so that best use could eventually be made of the land. Marked animals were observed and recorded, so that a movement and migration pattern would emerge; this, in turn, would give an idea of the carrying capacity of the range. He wanted to know which wild and which domestic animals thrive best in fertile or on brittle, easily eroded soil. Would domestic species turn arid earth into desert while the wild animals who have always lived there, preclude such a tragedy?

Toni, waiting for Dick to find a fairly resident group of animals, wanted to instrument them so that their adaptation to that kind of environment could be investigated. This was a practical, very essential kind of study and Dick, with a wealth of experience behind him, moved calmly from place to place, enduring or brushing aside the many difficulties which are naturally associated with any pioneering work.

When the rains ceased, Toni and Dick and I joined forces and went to Amboseli Game Reserve where Dick had been marking game for some time. It was just before we were due to go to Manyara and Toni thought this a wonderful chance to 'get his eye in' again, for he had been through a long period of office desk and lecture theatre, with too little bush action in between. I loved Amboseli. If we were lucky, we might glimpse Kilimanjaro, the 20,000-foot snow-covered mountain, so named by the Masai people, for to them he is the 'little hill', the 'footstool of the Lord'.

We were not disappointed. On the morning after our arrival the mountain was in clear view, though the elephants, as though sensing our purpose in coming, were not to be seen anywhere. We drove to the top of Kitirua hill and from there, with the aid of binoculars, scanned the countryside, finding almost every kind of animal, except the elusive pachyderm. After almost an hour we decided to search the forest at the edge of the dry lake basin and here, at last, we spotted a fairly large, 9,000-pounder. As he stopped after a mock charge, and turned, Toni put a dart into the shoulder, a good site from which the drug substance becomes rapidly absorbed.

We followed at a respectful distance as he walked off, finally stopping in his tracks thirty-eight minutes after darting. Ten minutes later he went down on to his brisket, a huge sphinx-like form, lying upright on the dusty ground, the soles of his huge feet turned strangely forwards, exposing the deeply furrowed undersurface of his soles. Dick found the circumference of each foot to be fifty-six inches while the height of the body, measuring from shoulder to the point of the foot, was ten feet.

'Time to inject the antidote,' Toni had called as soon as one red disc had been fixed on to each ear; exactly ten seconds after his syringe-full had been emptied the grey shape had risen, bat-like, and sent us scuttling into the vehicle.

Decorated thus he made off towards the forest at the side of the lake basin, dry and full of heat haze mirages at this time of the year. We followed for over an hour, hoping to get a photograph of his 'new look' from the front, but there was nothing doing. He had had enough and the men had to content themselves with side-view shots. Weeks later, when Toni returned to see his special weighing machine in operation on immobilized antelope, the ear markings were still there.

But something else was missing. Odinga, the famous, huge, friendly elephant of Amboseli, who had featured in numerous books on wildlife, who was beloved of visitors and rangers alike, was no more. Toni and Dick had intended to immobilize him to stave off just such a disaster as had overtaken him, for they were going to engrave his much-coveted tusks with the words: 'Property of Amboseli Game Reserve' in silver nitrate, a substance that does not fade with time.

The local game warden had told them the sad tale on arrival; Odinga had once again moved outside the boundaries of his home sanctuary and they had been waiting for him: the professional hunter and the trophy collector, unable to control their lust to kill or their ambition to possess, even for a venerable old elephant considered to be part and parcel of the Reserve.

Slowly the news spread but it took a long time before those who had known and admired Odinga really believed that he was no more. Disbelief, disgust at the lack of reverence of the hunter and his client were freely expressed. Many tales about the great old elephant were retold, mostly new to me, which demonstrated his nobility, his lack of viciousness. He had, on several occasions, had the chance to kill or to injure but had never done so. Once he had actually stood over the helpless figure of an over-venturesome visitor who had tripped and fallen as Odinga had chased him within the camp. As soon as the chase was over and the quarry at bay, he had shaken his enormous head and ears and had ambled off, perhaps amused at the little game he had played.

Many have had proof of the superlative intelligence, the mystic regard of death, the sense of social responsibility, the mischievous humour and the proud, disdainful awareness which the elephant displays towards man. What motivated the elephants who tore out the tusks of a dead mate before the hunter could reach him, and carried them far afield to a place which was never discovered? Or the elephant bull who, in full sight of the ranger of a southern Game Sanctuary, delivered a deadly accurate death thrust into the brain of an ailing cow? There is much evidence that elephant cover up the dead, human or their own kind, and that they aid each other in time of danger or difficulty.

What, after all, does man know about the workings of the mind of an elephant, or indeed of any creature, including man? Working among the wild should teach respect, humility. Whether close-range study, hunting or cropping, the importance of which cannot be denied, or long-distance observation, it should make no difference. Our task is to maintain that which we have been given and to try to understand the nature of the gift. Looking at our world, man's world, through the eyes of an elephant might be most enlightening. Perhaps he accepts us more readily into his realm than we, in our present ignorance, accept him into ours, especially as we seem to possess nothing that he wants, except space to live in. We, on the other hand, seem not only to want him alive to grace our recreational parks but also dead to provide us with those trophies which man seems to need to boost his own ego.

As his answer to a hunter, who seemed unable to conceive Africa as anything but pounds of ivory, the author-naturalist, Colin Fletcher, made this reply:

Animals are not just curiosities crossing the landscape, but are part of the complex web of the whole of existence of which man is, at present, *the* dominant species. That, however, does not give us the right to assume that the world was made for man. From the elephant's point of view, the world was designed for elephants.

Had these words been carved on a notice board on the way to Amboseli, Odinga's life might have been saved. . . .

INDEX